My Very Own Story

A play for children

Alan Ayckbourn

Samuel French — London
New York - Toronto - Hollywood

MY VERY OWN STORY

First performed at the Stephen Joseph Theatre in the Round, Scarborough, on 10th August, 1991, with the following cast:

The Story-tellers

Percy Parton	Peter Bourke
Peter Patchett	Crispin Letts
Paul Peel	James Simmons
Keyboard Player	John Pattison

The Characters
Percy's Story — *The Donkey*

Rupert	James Simmons
Gorff	Robert Austin
Yerp	Jeffrey Chiswick
Mrs Yerp	Elizabeth Kelly
Frederick	Glyn Grain
Leonora	Rebecca Lacey

Peter's Story — *The Enchanted Suitor*

Frederick	Peter Bourke
Alicia	Anna Keaveney
Cecilia	Isabel Lloyd
Emilia	Elizabeth Rider

Paul's Story — *The Sorceror's Daughter*

Varius	Crispin Letts
Cecilia/Alicia	Isabel Lloyd
Alicia/Cecilia	Anna Keaveney
Emilia	Elizabeth Rider
Denzil	Gary Whitaker
Basil	Robert Austin
Village Boy	Jeffrey Chiswick

Directed by Alan Ayckbourn
Musical Direction by John Pattison
Designed by Juliet Nichols
Lighting by Jackie Staines

CHARACTERS

The Story-tellers
Percy Parton
Peter Patchett
Paul Peel
Keyboard Player

Actor

The Characters
Percy's Story — *The Donkey*
Rupert (played by **Paul**)
Gorff, the coachman
Mrs Yerp
Yerp, her husband, Leonora and Frederick's retainer
Leonora
Frederick, Leonora's brother (the "donkey")

Peter's Story — *The Enchanted Suitor*
Frederick as a young man (played by **Percy**)
1st Woman
2nd Woman
Plain Woman
Cecilia, who marries Frederick
Alicia, her mother
Emilia, her sister

Paul's Story —*The Sorceror's Daughter*
Cecilia/Alicia
Alicia/Cecilia
Emilia
Varius, Alicia's husband (played by **Peter**)
Village Boy
Denzil
Basil

The action takes place on an empty stage

Time — the present

**Other plays by Alan Ayckbourn published by
Samuel French Ltd:**

ACT I

A stage

A keyboard player is visible to the audience, at the side or in the orchestra pit. He plays as the audience enters

Percy sticks his head round the edge of the proscenium and signals. The keyboard player plays a fanfare. Percy disappears

Percy enters

Percy Thank you, thank you. You're very kind. Splendid. Marvellous. My name is Percy Parton and may I say straight away how delighted I was to receive your invitation to come along here today to entertain you with this, my very own story. Please remember, ladies and gentlemen, if you will, that what you are about to witness here in a few moments' time is my very own personal, individual, singular and utterly original narrative. Remember where you heard it first — from me, the horse's mouth. (*He laughs*) But seriously, enough of that and, as we often say in the magical world of the theatre, on with the show. May I first of all introduce to you the people who will be assisting me today. Taking care of music and melody, on keyboards Mr Reg Cord.

The keyboard player plays a fanfare and acknowledges the audience

Secondly, those most important people who will be taking part in my very own story — ladies and gentlemen — the actors!

The actors come on, bow briefly and go off again

Now, do bear with me, ladies and gentlemen, I have outside in the taxi — which is still ticking over, incidentally — one or two small props and additional items which we will be using to assist us with our story-telling. I won't be one moment, I promise. Perhaps in the meantime I could ask Mr Cord, if he would, to entertain you with a selection of brief musical moments. Won't be one second. Don't go away. Thank you, Mr Cord.

Percy exits

As Percy goes off, the keyboard player begins to play again, as at the start

After a moment, from a different direction, Peter sticks his head round the edge of the proscenium. He signals to the keyboard player who plays a fanfare. He disappears

Peter enters

Peter Thank you, everyone, so very much. You're most kind. I must apologize for being a tiny bit late. Blame the traffic. Hallo, my name is Peter Patchett and may I say, right at the start, how delighted I was to receive your invitation to come along here today to entertain you with this, my very own story. Never forget, ladies and gentlemen, if you will, that what you are about to witness here in just a second or two will be my own personal, unique, singular and quintessentially original narrative. Avoid cheap imitations, insist only on the original — yours truly! (*He laughs*) But enough mirth for the present and, as we often say in the wondrous world of the theatre, let's get this show on the road. May I first of all, though, introduce you to the people who will be assisting me today. Taking care of music and melody, on keyboards, Mr Bill Notes, ladies and gentlemen.

The keyboard player plays a fanfare and acknowledges the audience. He looks a bit puzzled

Secondly, those people who will be taking part in my very own story — ladies and gentlemen — the players themselves!

The actors come on, looking a little puzzled. They bow briefly and go off again

Now, you're going to have to excuse me just one second, ladies and gentlemen. I have to fetch one or two small properties and technical items from my van outside, I'm afraid. I won't be one moment. I do so apologize. Meanwhile, I will ask Mr Notes if he'd be good enough to entertain you with a few lingering magical musical moments. Won't be one second. Stay right there. Take it away, Mr Notes.

Peter exits

As Peter goes off, the keyboard player begins to play again, as at the start

After a moment, Percy hurries back on with a suitcase of props, which he puts to one side of the stage

Percy Won't keep you long. Carry on, Mr Cord.

Percy hurries off

From a different direction, Paul sticks his head round the edge of the proscenium. He signals to the keyboard player who plays a fanfare. He disappears

Paul enters, rather breathless

Paul Look, I'm terribly late I know and I do sincerely beg your pardon, all of you. I'm afraid we have British Rail to thank for this. My name is Paul Peel and believe me I'm delighted to be here at long last. Thank you for asking me. And for your patience. I won't waste a moment longer of your time. Just quickly to put you in the picture. What you're about to hear is my incomparable, unparalleled, supremely distinctive, highly individual, very own story. Beware of cheap imitations, insist on the original — me. (*He laughs*) But — no time for jokes, let us, as we show business people are wont to say, ring up the curtain. But before we do that, I must first introduce to you the people who will be assisting me today. Taking care of music and melody — on keyboards, ladies and gentlemen, Mr Brian Tune.

The keyboard player plays a fanfare and acknowledges the audience. He looks even more puzzled

And now for those special people who will be playing various roles in my very own story today — ladies and gentlemen — the performers!

The actors come on, as before, although now they seem thoroughly confused and a bit cross. They bow briefly and go off again

Listen, I'm afraid I'm going to have to crave just one more smidgin of your patience. I've got a couple of bags of stuff outside I have to bring in before we can start, I do beg your pardon. So I'm going to ask Mr Tune here if he'd mind playing you a few myriad melodies, just for a quick second. Would you mind most awfully, Mr Tune? Thank you. Won't be a tick.

Paul exits

As Paul goes off, the keyboard player begins to play again, as at the start

After a moment, Peter hurries back with a box of props which he puts at one side of the stage

Peter (*smiling at the audience*) Nearly there. Keep going, Mr Notes.

Peter exits

Percy enters, carrying another case, which he puts to one side with the other one

Percy (*smiling at the audience*) That's the lot. Just going to pay the taxi. Thank you, Mr Cord, keep up the good work.

Percy exits

Paul enters with a bag of props which he puts at the side of the stage

Paul One more. Hang on. Carry on, Mr Tune.

Paul exits

Peter enters with another box of props which he puts with the first

Peter That's it. Sorry to keep you. Just got to lock the van. Bravo, Mr Notes, thank you.

Peter exits

Percy enters

Percy All right now, thank you for waiting. And thank you, Mr Cord, thank you, Reg. A big hand for Reg Cord, ladies and gentlemen.

Percy leads the applause. The keyboard player acknowledges this

Thank you, thank you. Now. Pay close attention, if you will. My very own story. Let us take a second to imagine, ladies and gentlemen, if you will, that we are in a dark, dark wood. Imagine that.

Percy pauses dramatically, eyes closed

Peter enters

Peter (*without noticing Percy*) Thank you, ladies and gentlemen, you've been very patient, thank you again and a special big thank you to Mr Notes for keeping us all entertained. Ladies and gentlemen, on keyboards, Mr Bill Notes. Thank you.

Peter leads the applause. The keyboard player acknowledges this. Percy stares in amazement

Thank you so much, you're very generous. Now, gather round everyone please for this, my very own story. It started one bright September morning when I was ——

Percy Hey! I say. Oy!

Peter What?

Percy I say — do you mind?

Peter Sorry. Do you mind?

Percy I'm saying, do you mind?

Peter Look, do you mind?

Percy No, no, I'm asking, do you mind ——?

Peter That's what I'm asking you, do you mind ——?

Percy No, I'm the one who's doing the asking. Do you mind?

Peter Well, yes, I do mind. I certainly do mind, if you don't mind.

Percy Me? I mind. Indeed I do mind. Never mind asking me if I mind, I'm asking you, do you mind?

Peter How many more times, yes I do. I mind very much.

Percy Well, so do I. So mind out of the way.

Peter Mind it, now, mind it.

Percy No, you mind it, mate, you're the one to mind it. I've a good mind to give you a piece of my mind in a minute, mind.

Peter I don't mind. See if I mind. You're out of your mind, anyway. I've half a mind to ——

Percy A mind to what? A mind to what?

Peter Never mind. (*Muttering*) Mindless git.

Percy (*threateningly*) Now, mind your language!

Peter Mind your own business!

They stand facing each other antagonistically

Paul enters with his second bag. He fails to notice the other two

Paul Thank you so much, ladies and gentlemen, and I do promise you that
will be our last delay, the very last one. And under the circumstances I think
a specially big hand for our noble keyboard player, Mr Tune, is in order.
Ladies and gentlemen, Mr Brian Tune ...

*Paul leads the applause. The keyboard player acknowledges this. Peter and
Percy stand stupefied*

Thank you so very much. Now, without further delay, off we go — my very
own story, chapter one. Imagine if you will, one wet afternoon in June. I
was just returning from ——

Percy } (*together*) Oy! I'm sorry ...
Peter

Paul (*puzzled*) Sorry?
Percy No, I'm sorry ...
Paul You're sorry? Sorry, I'm the one that should be sorry, surely ——
Peter There's no point in being sorry now, is there?

A slight pause as they stare at each other

Percy (*muttering*) Well, this is a sorry state of affairs.
Paul Sorry?
Percy Sorry, I was just ...

They look at each other. Another pause

Peter I think we ought to sort this out, don't you?
Percy We should.
Paul It's perfectly simple. I've every right to be here and you two haven't.
That's the long and the short of it.
Percy Is it now?
Paul Yes.
Peter Really?
Paul It most certainly is.
Percy Please excuse us one minute, ladies and gentlemen.
Peter One moment ——
Paul Just one second. Music please, Mr Tune ——
Percy Mr Cord ——
Peter Mr Notes ——

The keyboard player, rather bewildered, starts to play feverishly

Percy (*rather quickly*) Quiet!
Peter *Quiet!*
Paul QUIET!!!

They keyboard player stops playing

Percy Listen, this can be sorted out very quickly. There's obviously been a
double — triple booking here. Quite easily sorted out. No need for
aggravation, I'm sure. After all, we're all members of the wonderful
brotherhood of show business — (*he produces a contract from his pocket*)
here we are, legal proof ... if proof is needed — (*reading*) "This agreement
between on the one hand the theatre company hereinafter known as the
employer and the undersigned hereinafter referred to as the entertainer" —
(*skipping a bit*) diddly-diddly-doo ... "I, Percy Parton, do hereby agree ——"
Peter (*reading from an identical contract he has produced*) "... I, Peter
Patchett, do hereby agree ——"
Paul (*doing likewise*) "... I, Paul Peel, do hereby agree ——"
Percy "— to abide ——"
Peter "— to abide ——"
Paul "— to abide ——"
Percy "— by ——"
Peter "— by ——"
Paul "— by ——"

They stare at each other

Percy (*grabbing Peter's contract*) Let me see that ——
Peter (*grabbing Paul's contract*) Let me see that ——
Paul (*grabbing Percy's contract*) Let me see that ——

They study the respective documents, muttering through the small print

Percy (*grabbing Paul's contract from Peter*) Let me see that ——
Peter (*grabbing Percy's contract from Paul*) Let me see that ——
Paul (*grabbing Peter's contract from Percy*) Let me see that ——

They study the respective documents, muttering as before

Percy That seems —— (*He hands Paul's contract back to Peter*)
Peter — to be —— (*He hands Percy's contract back to Paul*)

Paul — in order —— (*He hands Peter's contract back to Percy*)
All — yes.

They glance at the contracts, realize they have the wrong ones and exchange yet again

   (*Together*) Yes.
Peter This needs thinking about.
Percy Yes.
Paul Yes.
Peter Mr Note ...
Percy Mr Cord ...
Paul Mr Tune ...

They ponder. The keyboard player starts to play again. He has barely started when:

Percy Just a moment!

They keyboard player stops

Peter (*startled*) What?
Paul (*similarly*) What is it?
Percy Listen, we are faced with a problem, right?
Peter Correct.
Paul True.
Percy Now, I may be wrong but it seems to me we have far too many story-tellers here.
Peter Two ——
Paul — too many.
Percy So. (*To Peter*) Either you leave ——
Paul Hear! Hear!
Peter Absolutely not ——
Percy (*to Paul*) Or you leave ——
Peter Brilliant.
Paul Out of the question ——
Percy Or I leave ——
Peter } (*together*) Good idea.
Paul }
Percy — which we won't even bother to discuss.

Slight pause

Peter So we're all staying.
Percy Exactly.
Paul Precisely.
Peter Well, we can't tell three stories, can we?
Percy Take all night.
Paul Right.
Peter In that case, we'd better all tell the same story.
Percy Well, you're certainly not going to tell my very own story.
Paul Nobody tells my very own story but me.
Peter Well, I was thinking we might tell my very own story, actually.
Percy Your very own story?
Paul Certainly not. It's yours.
Peter Just an idea.

Slight pause

An Actor enters

Actor Excuse me ...
Percy Yes?
Peter Yes?
Paul What is it?
Actor Will we be starting soon ——?
Percy In a minute ——
Actor — only the lads are getting a bit restless ——
Peter — two seconds ——
Actor —— only we've been bowing a lot, you see, but not a lot of acting ...
Paul Literally, half a second ...
Actor Sorry to trouble you.
Percy Not at all.

The Actor exits

Paul I think ——
Percy Yes?
Peter Yes?
Paul I think the only way around this, is to decide it by chance.
Percy We could draw for it.
Peter Lots?
Percy Well, once or twice. Just till we decide.
Paul I've got it. The yes or no game. We all keep talking but none of us can

say yes or no. If we say yes or no, we're out of the game. Last one in wins. What about that, then?

Percy
Peter } (*together*) No.

They keyboard player makes a gong sound. He makes this sound for each subsequent "yes" and "no" during the game

Paul Right, you're both out. I win.
Percy We weren't ready.
Peter Not ready.
Percy Anyway, it's a stupid game you can never win it.
Paul Yes, you can.

Gong

Percy Right, that's you out.
Paul I wasn't playing.
Percy (*to Peter*) You heard him, he said it, didn't he?
Peter Yes.

Gong

Percy Right that's you out too, I win.
Peter I wasn't ready.
Paul He didn't say anything, did he?
Percy Yes, he did.

Gong

Paul Right, that's you out ——
Percy Just a minute, just a minute ——
Peter All right. Start again. This is the real start. OK? The real start of the game. Both ready?
Percy (*carefully*) I am ready.
Paul I am quite ready.

Silence

Peter Somebody say something.
Percy Why?
Peter Because we can't decide the game unless somebody says something, can we?

Pause

Paul Very nice weather, isn't it?
Percy When?
Paul Lately.
Peter Where?
Paul Up — there — in the sky.

Pause

Peter (*suddenly; to Paul*) Sorry, did you say something?
Paul No.

Gong

Peter Out!
Paul That wasn't fair.
Percy Out!
Peter Just me and you.
Percy Just us.

Silence

Peter (*suddenly, as before*) Sorry. Did you say something?
Percy Who me?
Peter Yes.

Gong

Percy Out!
Peter That was cheating.
Paul Out!
Percy I win. Now, my very own story ——
Peter What do we do, then?
Paul What happens to us?
Percy I don't know. Goodbye, then.
Peter Goodbye?
Percy Off you go.
Paul Go?
Percy So long.

Peter But we ——
Percy Cheerio.
Paul We ——
Percy Ta-ta.

Paul and Peter exit reluctantly

Paul returns

Paul What about all our — (*he indicates the bags of props, etc.*)
Percy Later. You can collect them later.

Paul exits

Ladies and gentlemen, at long last My Very Own Story. It is a tragic
Victorian tale entitled, *The Donkey*.

Music. The Lights change

Imagine it is night time in a dark wood, a few days before a Christmas many
long forgotten years ago. It is bitterly cold, a sharp, slicing, biting wind;
thick snow lies on the ground. Snow so deep that it is now almost
impossible to make out the rough cart track that winds between the trunks
of the huge tall trees. Very few people venture this way in weather such as
this and rarely, if ever, at night. Yet it was along this very path on that day
before Christmas Eve that I, Rupert Fellowes, found myself travelling
alone. I was intending to spend the holidays with my brother and his family.
They had recently moved away from our home and we had consequently
lost touch. I was now anxious to see both him and his wife, and most
especially my angelic little nephews and nieces for whom I had bought a
whole trunk-load of gifts and presents. I confess though that when I set out,
I had no idea what a remote and God-forsaken district they had chosen for
their new home. Difficult to reach even in midsummer, the recent snow-
storms had made their village all but inaccessible. Indeed, few local
coachmen would agree to venture out at all and I had nearly given up hope
of finding a driver. Then one particular fellow named Gorff approached me
and offered his services. Had I not been so anxious for transportation, I
might have realized that his willingness to convey me concealed an evil and
ulterior design.

*At this point the "coach" enters. It is driven by Gorff, an evil looking
coachman. In the back is Paul, muffled up and unrecognizable in coat,*

scarf and hat. He is shaken about as Gorff struggles with his "horses"

Gorff (*cursing*) Gwaaan ... Gooworm ... gwaaarn, yer bleezers ... yup ... yurr ... gworrn ...

Percy This Gorff was certainly an evil-looking enough fellow but I prided myself on never judging others on first appearances. The journey was, though, one of the most thoroughly uncomfortable I had ever undergone. Gorff's coach could well have benefited from care and attention, his horses from food and better treatment, and his passengers from a little consideration.

Gorff Whooyer ... whooa ... wheeerr ... whooorrrr!

Gorff reins back the horses and the coach stops

Percy Unexpectedly, the coach pulled up with a shuddering suddenness. I must confess the abrupt lack of motion was a considerable physical relief. I wondered what the cause of our stopping might be. I leant out of the window and called to the man.

Paul I say — I say, what's happening? Why have we stopped, coachman?

Percy The man Gorff, by way of reply, climbed down off the box seat, muttering incomprehensibly.

Gorff climbs down, muttering

Gorff Mun git down wearn stuckinasnow ...

Paul What's that you say?

Gorff Stuckinasnow ... (*He gesticulates to demonstrate*) Stuckin! Stuckin!

Paul Stuckin? Oh, stuck in ...

Gorff Ar. Stuckinasnow ...

Paul Ah! Stuck in the snow. Oh yes, quite. I see. Are we? Oh dear ...

Gorff Git darn. Mun git darn.

Paul Mun git darn?

Gorff Ye mun git darn.

Paul Mun git darn?

Gorff *Ye* mun git darn.

Paul You mean *me* mun git darn? Ah. Mun git darn?

Percy I confessed to a certain difficulty understanding the fellow.

Gorff (*insistently*) Git darn.

Paul Git darn? Git darn? What on earth can he mean? Oh, you mean get down. You want me to git darn ...?

Gorff Git darn on the grarn.

Paul On the grarn. Right. (*He climbs out*)

Percy It was bitterly cold out of the coach.

Paul Brrr!

Gorff Mun pushem. (*Demonstrating*) Pushem, see?

Paul Pushem, yes. You want me to pushem, do you?

Gorff Ar. (*He moves off and starts to climb up again*)

Paul Righty-ho. What are you going to do?

Gorff Pullem. Oi mun pullem.

Paul Oh, I see. You're going to pullem. I'll pushem, you pullem. Fair enough.

Gorff Uroit!

Paul Say when. I'm ready. (*He braces himself against the back of the coach*)

Gorff Uroit!

Paul Er — right.

Gorff (*whipping up the horses*) Giddy — or — arrr! Hup!

He moves off rapidly. Paul falls over in the snow

   Gorff exits

Paul Grooo!

Percy And to my horror, before I could prevent him, the fellow had whipped up the horses and in a trice had galloped into the night, leaving me face down in the snow.

Paul Hoy!

Percy I clambered to my feet and shouted after the fellow, cursing him roundly in no uncertain terms ——

Paul (*calling after Gorff*) Rogue! Villain! Scoundrel!

Percy — but to no avail. My voice was all but lost in the increasing blizzard. I looked around me for signs of assistance but I was completely alone and helplessly lost. The knave had taken everything I owned. My hip flask, my travelling rug, all my luggage and, worse still, all the Christmas presents intended for my angelic little nephews and nieces.

Paul Blackguard! (*He shivers*)

Percy I knew if I failed to find shelter soon I would swiftly perish from the cold; but in what direction to walk, I had little idea. I was, I confess, hopelessly lost now, as the last evidence of the cart track disappeared under ever deepening snow. I walked for what seemed miles and miles; but for all I know, in circles.

Paul Help! Help!

Percy The cold wind sliced like a dagger through my clothes, my limbs grew wearier, my voice weaker ...

Paul (*feebly*) Help!

Percy And I resigned myself to death ...

Paul sits huddled for a moment. Throughout the following he acts simultaneously with the narration

Then — all of a sudden — I caught sight of something.

There is a distant glimmer of lamplight

A distant glimmer, a glint of — could it be lamplight — yes — through that thick curtain of snowflakes ... something! I struggled to my feet ... I was feeble now and had reached the limit of my strength. Somehow I managed to stagger towards that ray of light, of hope, of life itself ...

Paul stops. The "doorway" of a "large stone building" — Deepwood House — becomes visible

The source of light was from a lamp illuminating the doorway of a large stone building — not quite a castle but certainly a house of some considerable size. Summoning my last gram of strength I crawled to the portal and knocked upon the door.

Hollow knocking. Paul waits

It seemed an age before anyone answered.

There is the rattling of chains and bolts and a final creak before Mrs Yerp, a housekeeper, opens the door

Mrs Yerp (*suspiciously*) Yes?
Paul (*faintly*) Excuse me ... I ... I'm sorry to trouble you I ... I'm sorry I ...
Percy But at that point my strength finally gave out.

Paul faints at Mrs Yerp's feet

Mrs Yerp (*alarmed*) Mr Yerp! Mr Yerp!

Yerp, the family retainer, hurries on

Yerp What's the matter, wife?
Mrs Yerp Help me. Help me with him, here.

During the following, Yerp and Mrs Yerp carry Paul inside the "house"

Leonora enters, pushing in a chaise-longue, *on which they lie Paul*

Percy Whilst I was still unconscious they must have carried me inside, I do not recall. How long I remained thus I cannot tell. But my next memory will remain with me for the rest of my life. When I awoke I found myself lying on a *chaise-longue* beside a log fire. As I opened my eyes fully, there standing before me, with a look of such tender compassion, a manner so demure and gentle, was the most beautiful woman I had ever seen in my life.

Leonora Help me to remove his outer garments, Mrs Yerp, they're soaked through ...

Mrs Yerp Yes, madam ...

Leonora Yerp, please build up the fire, he must be kept warm.

Yerp Yes, ma'am.

They remove Paul's coat, hat and scarf, revealing him for the first time

Paul (*groaning*) Aaah!

Leonora He's regaining consciousness, quickly ...

Paul (*groggily*) Who — who — waaa ... way ——

Leonora We must fetch blankets ...

Percy (*recognizing Paul for the first time*) Just a minute. Hold it a minute ...

The tableau freezes

You, yes, you.

Paul Me?

Percy What are you doing in my story?

Paul What do you think I'm doing? I'm playing Rupert.

Percy Rupert? Who said you could play Rupert?

Paul They did.

Percy They?

Paul Them back there. They said I could.

Percy What's it got to do with them?

Paul They said to me "You can play him," they said. "You look a right Rupert".

Percy Rubbish. You don't look anything like him. Get off at once. Where's the real bloke? The one who's supposed to be doing him?

Paul He's playing cards.

Percy Playing cards? I'm paying for him. Get him out here.

Leonora (*coming out of character*) Oh, leave him alone, he's good, this one.
Percy (*startled*) What?
Mrs Yerp (*likewise abandoning her character*) He is. He's brilliant.
Yerp He's great.
Leonora He's better than the other one.
Mrs Yerp Great improvement.
Yerp Certainly is ...
Paul Thank you very much ——
Percy Listen, what are you lot playing at? What's going on here?

During the following the other actors gather on the stage in varying stages of dress and undress. Several of them have been disturbed from a card game

Leonora Oh, go on ...
Mrs Yerp Go on ...
Yerp Go on ...
Percy Whose story is this, anyway?
Leonora Oh, get on with it ——
Paul ⎫   ⎧ Yes, get on with it ——
Mrs Yerp ⎬ (*together*) ⎨ Get on with it ——
Yerp ⎭   ⎩ Get on!
Percy (*trying to be heard*) Just a minute ...!
Actors (*variously*) Get on ... get on with it, ... go on ... *etc.*
Percy (*shouting them down*) All right! *All right*! ALL RIGHT!

Silence

(*Sulkily*) But I should have been asked first. This is my very own story and I should have been asked.

The actors go off again

The others resume their tableau

Carry on, then. (*Pause*) Where were we?
Leonora I was asking them to fetch blankets.
Percy Well go on, then ...
Leonora We must fetch blankets ...
Mrs Yerp Yes, madam.
Leonora And more logs for the fire ...
Yerp Yes, ma'am.

Yerp and Mrs Yerp exit

Percy I gazed in wonder at this beautiful woman.
Paul Who are you? Where am I?
Percy (*muttering*) He's not right for Rupert at all.
Leonora My name is Leonora Stringer. You are in Deepwood House. Mrs Yerp found you on our doorstep, half dead. How did you come to be here, on a night like this?
Paul I was ... I —— (*He tries to get up but feels giddy*)
Leonora No, don't try to stand, you're exhausted. You need food and then you must sleep.
Paul My name is Rupert Fellowes. I need to reach my brother's house tonight. They're expecting me ...
Leonora Where does he live?
Paul In Thornglade Village. Is it far?
Leonora Not too far. But you can't possibly travel there tonight. You must at least wait until morning.

Mrs Yerp returns with a blanket

Mrs Yerp, we will dine immediately, please.
Mrs Yerp Yes, madam. But what about the master?
Leonora He — will probably join us — in due course.
Mrs Yerp Very good, madam.
Leonora And Mrs Yerp ...
Mrs Yerp Yes, madam?
Leonora You had better warn my brother we have company tonight.
Mrs Yerp Yes, madam.

Mrs Yerp exits

Paul You live with your brother, Miss Stringer?
Leonora (*frowning*) Yes. I do, Mr Fellowes.
Percy At the mention of her brother, her smooth and quite flawless complexion became marred by the hint of a frown. I was to note this phenomenon on future occasions whenever he was present or his name mentioned.

Yerp enters, pushing on a dining-table. Mrs Yerp follows with two chairs. She places one at the end of the table and another at the centre

Yerp Dinner is served, madam.
Leonora Thank you, Yerp. (*To Paul*) Please, Mr Fellowes — (*indicating the centre chair*) sit here.

Yerp exits

Paul rises and sways

(*Alarmed*) Can you manage?
Paul Yes, I'm fine, Miss Stringer. I'm perfectly fine.
Mrs Yerp (*offering her arm*) Sir ...
Paul Thank you. Thank you.

Mrs Yerp guides him to the table. He sits. Leonora sits as well

Yerp returns with a third dining chair which he places at the head of the table

Mrs Yerp starts to serve dinner. Yerp assists her

Yerp and Mrs Yerp exit when the meal is served

Percy The dinner was superb and my hostess never less than completely charming. Nonetheless, I could not entirely ignore the frequent and anxious glances she gave either towards the doorway or to the empty chair at the other end of the table.
Paul It's a great pity your brother is missing this delicious meal. May I enquire, will he soon be joining us?
Leonora It is of no consequence either way, Mr Fellowes. Frederick — my brother — wouldn't, couldn't eat this at all, I fear. He's on a rather strict and special diet.
Paul Oh, dear.
Leonora For his health, that is all.
Paul Can he not eat meat?
Leonora Oh, no. Nor fish, nor game nor most vegetables.
Paul How tragic. What is wrong with him?
Leonora He's ——

Frederick enters

Percy But before she could answer, the door burst open and I caught my first glimpse of her brother, Frederick Stringer.

Frederick crosses to the table and sits without looking at either Paul or Leonora. He gazes ahead of him with a tortured expression

If two natures in a brother and sister could ever be described as opposing then here indeed was a striking example. The one temperament sunny and outgoing, the other dark and withdrawn. The man entered the room but chose to ignore both of us completely.

Paul (*half rising*) Good-evening, sir.

Frederick ignores him

Leonora (*gently*) Frederick, dear, this is Mr Fellowes.

Silence

He was trapped in the storm and lost his way.

Silence

He will be staying here for the night with us, if that is satisfactory.

Percy But the brother sat as though unable to hear his sister at all.

Paul (*to himself*) How could one ignore such a divine creature as this?

Leonora You must excuse my brother, Mr Fellowes. Sometimes he ... he ... is lost in contemplation.

Paul Do not let it trouble you for an instant, Miss Stringer. I fully understand.

Mrs Yerp enters and starts to serve Frederick his meal. She exits as soon as this task is completed

Percy After the appearance of the brother, the meal took on a more sombre tone as we lapsed into silence. In the absence of conversation, I could not help but observe the food that was being served to the brother, Frederick. It was indeed singular fare. Large helpings of what appeared to be nothing more nor less than long grass, prettily served from a silver salver and accompanied — could my eyes be deceiving me? — by a salad of common or garden thistles.

Paul (*incredulously*) Thistles?

Leonora I beg your pardon, Mr Fellowes? Did you speak?

Paul No, Miss Stringer. I was merely remarking on the delicious quality of the food.

Leonora Oh.

Percy It was not until the very end of the meal that Mr Stringer was to utter his first words.

Frederick Leonora, I note that we have company. I was not informed of this.

Leonora Oh, I am sorry, my dear, I did ——

Paul (*getting up and extending his hand*) How do you do, sir. My name is ——

Frederick (*rising abruptly*) Good-night to you, sir.

Frederick exits

Silence

Leonora You really must excuse my brother, Mr Fellowes, he is ... he is ...

Paul (*helpfully*) Lost in contemplation, perhaps?

Leonora (*gratefully*) Precisely. He contemplates more and more these days.

Paul An admirable quality and one we would all of us be wise to emulate, Miss Stringer.

Percy But secretly I observed the man to be both uncouth and ungallant. How could brother and sister be so different?

Leonora (*rising and drifting to the door*) Allow me to show you to your room, Mr Fellowes, you must be quite exhausted.

Paul But for the stimulation and excitement of the company, madam, I confess I would have fallen asleep an hour ago.

Leonora (*smiling*) You are too kind, Mr Fellowes.

Percy She and I were getting on like a house on fire.

They both move away to a "bedchamber" area — possibly the chaise-longue

I allowed the delicate creature to lead me to my bedchamber.

Leonora If everything is to your satisfaction, I will bid you good-night, Mr Fellowes.

Paul Please, Miss Stringer, I would much prefer it if you were to call me Rupert.

Leonora Very well. If you so wish you may call me Leonora.

Paul Leonora.

Leonora Good-night, Rupert.

Paul Good-night, Leonora.

Leonora exits

Paul, in due course, lies down

During the following, Yerp and Mrs Yerp enter and re-arrange the table for breakfast

Percy Once she had gone, leaving me with only the delicate aroma of her perfume and the soft lingering memory of her final haunting smile, I fell upon the bed fully dressed and was instantly asleep. My slumber was uninterrupted but for one strange occurrence that awoke me just before dawn.

The distant braying of a donkey is heard. Paul sits up, startled. Yerp and Mrs Yerp listen as well for a moment, then resume their tasks

What on earth could have been the source of such an unearthly sound I could not begin to guess.

Yerp exits

Paul lies back in his bed. Immediately a cock crows and he sits up again

During the following, Leonora enters and sits at the table, and Paul makes his way to join her

The following morning I awoke fully refreshed, dressed swiftly and hurried downstairs in search of breakfast. For I confess, despite last night's splendid repast, I was again ravenous.

Paul sits. During the following Mrs Yerp serves breakfast

A little to my surprise, considering the hour, Leonora was already breakfasting.

Leonora Good-morning, Rupert.

Paul Good-morning, Leonora.

Percy Her complexion seemed a trifle pale, her manner somewhat distracted.

Leonora I trust you slept well?

Paul Extremely well, thank you. And you?

Leonora I — have had a little trouble lately in sleeping ... I ——

Paul Indeed. I am sorry to hear that. (*To Mrs Yerp*) Thank you.

Leonora It is nothing, I assure you. It will pass, I expect. (*Softly*) As most things do in time.

Slight pause

Paul (*brightly*) Certainly your brother does not seem to share your affliction.

Leonora (*startled from her reverie*) What?

Paul Your brother. Frederick. I conclude, from his absence at this table, that he sleeps better than any of us. (*He laughs rather nervously*)

Mrs Yerp stares at him sharply

Unless of course he is already up and about.

Leonora (*her eyes closed*) He is indeed up. And about.

Paul I see. I apologize, then. (*He laughs*) Perhaps ——

Leonora gives a barely controlled sob

(*Concerned*) Miss Stringer ... Leonora ... (*He attempts to place his hand on hers to console her*)

At his touch, Leonora rises and rushes from the room. Her crying can be heard, receding along the passage

Paul rises as if to follow

Mrs Yerp (*rather firmly*) Indian or Chinese tea, sir.

Paul Err ... Chindian. Inese, rather. I mean ...

Mrs Yerp A little of each, sir.

Paul (*sitting*) Mrs Yerp, is there anything ...? Is there?

Mrs Yerp Nothing that need concern you, sir.

Paul It's just that Miss ——

Mrs Yerp She'll be perfectly all right, sir, I can assure you. The minute you've gone.

Paul Me? It is I who am the cause of her upset? Surely not.

Mrs Yerp My advice, sir, for what it's worth, is to quit this house as soon as possible.

Paul Indeed?

Mrs Yerp It's a damned house, sir. Lived in by a doomed family.

Paul I don't understand. Miss Stringer seems to me ——

Mrs Yerp Mr Yerp, my husband, he set off for the village at five o'clock this morning. He'll be back with a horse for you by noon if he don't get trapped by the snow meantimes.

Paul Seven hours to ride to the village and back? Is it that far?

Mrs Yerp He won't be riding there, sir. Only riding back.

Paul Then how is he getting there? Not walking, surely?

Mrs Yerp Ay.

Paul You have no horses here?

Mrs Yerp No, sir. The master and mistress won't have them. Won't have them on the property.

Paul Why on earth not?

Mrs Yerp That's their choice, sir. It's not for us to question.

Paul But what if there was an emergency? What if you needed, say, a doctor? Do you hope to walk to the village in the event of a crisis?

Mrs Yerp If there's a crisis then we runs, sir. Will there be anything further you require?

Paul No, no ... A splendid breakfast. Thank you, Mrs Yerp.

Mrs Yerp Thank you, sir.

Paul rises

Mrs Yerp exits, pushing the table away

Paul moves out into the "grounds"

Percy There being no further sign of my host or hostess, I resolved, since the weather appeared to have improved, to walk a little in the gardens. Although covered in snow, this gave the house and the outbuildings an almost fairy-tale beauty. For the life of me, I could detect nothing in the least damned, let alone doomed, about the place. I did not venture far for fear of getting lost but the grounds were quite large enough to provide me with an exhilarating two-hour walk around their perimeter. When I returned, expecting to find Mr Yerp back from the village with my horse, I was to be disappointed. There was no sign of the man.

Mrs Yerp enters and clears up the chairs

Paul It is now past noon, has Mr Yerp not returned?

Mrs Yerp No, sir.

Paul Oh, dear ...

Mrs Yerp The snow'll probably be deep around Keeper's Lug.

Paul I see. It's just my brother is expecting me. Was expecting me. Yesterday.

Mrs Yerp I dare say my husband's trying his level best, sir.

She exits

Paul (*calling after her*) I have no doubt.

Percy I determined, rather than wait about, to walk the perimeter back the other way. Thus I took another two-hour stroll around the grounds. When

I returned, to my dismay, there was still no sign of the wretched Yerp. I had to conclude that he had in all probability fallen into a snow-drift.

Paul (*calling*) I say ... I say ...

Mrs Yerp enters

Mrs Yerp Sir?

Paul Is there still no sign yet of him?

Mrs Yerp No, sir. 'Fraid not. He'll be stuck in Swine's Bottom, most like.

Paul But it will soon be dark. I really must start on my way. Have you no other transport of any kind?

Mrs Yerp None at all, sir. Like I said. Excuse me.

She exits

Percy Pleasant as they were, I could not face another two-hour walk around those grounds. Instead I decided this time to explore closer to the house itself. It was whilst I did this that I discovered in a high stone wall, a small concealed entrance that had previously escaped my notice. Unable to resist curiosity I tried the handle, half expecting the door to be locked. To my amazement it opened easily and upon stepping through it I found myself in a small walled paddock. The snow here had all but been cleared, a not inconsiderable task. But for me the source of far greater interest was the creature standing motionless in a far corner of the enclosure, its eyes fixed intently upon me. It was — to my utter amazement — no less a beast than a donkey. I cried out in surprise:

Frederick enters as the "donkey". He stands watching Paul

Paul Good heavens!

The donkey brays

(*Coaxingly*) Come on then. Come on, girl. Boy.

Percy Why they had lied to me was a mystery. Why had they told me that they had no transport, nothing that could carry me to the village? When it was clear even to one as untutored as myself that this sturdy little creature was more than adequate for the task. In a moment, my mind was made up. The hour was not late and if I was to avoid travelling in darkness I must leave this very minute. Having no luggage was, as it transpired, an advantage. I resolved to borrow this creature temporarily in order to reach the village. There I would leave it for Mr Yerp to recover. There could

surely be no harm in that. But first to catch the beast, who seemed from what
I knew of such creatures, unnaturally shy.

Paul (*coaxing the donkey*) Come on, boy. That's it, boy — I'm not going to
hurt you ...

*A sequence: Paul coaxes and tries to catch Frederick, the donkey. Frederick
backs away braying, Paul tries to corner him. At last he succeeds*

Percy He was an evasive brute but at last I succeeded ——
Paul Got you! Success. Now, to mount you.

Paul struggles to climb upon Frederick

Percy I must confess the task proved extremely difficult. It was the most
reluctant of steeds.
Paul Come on! Come on! Whooaa! Whoa! Steady! Easy!

A lot more braying. Paul finally "mounts"

All right, my beauty. Just as far as the village and then I'll set you free again,
I promise. You have my word. Yup there!
Percy But scarcely had we taken three paces outside the paddock ...

Mrs Yerp enters hurriedly

Mrs Yerp (*agitatedly*) No!!! No, you mustn't! You can't!
Paul I'm sorry, Mrs Yerp. I can wait no longer, I fear. The beast will be
returned, I promise.
Mrs Yerp No, please sir, no. You mustn't, please. If you do that you'll ...

Frederick suddenly rears up and gallops about. Paul holds on tightly

Percy (*simultaneously with the action*) But before the wretched woman
could finish, the donkey suddenly reared up and set off at a most terrifying
gallop ...
Paul (*alarmed*) Whooa!

Mrs Yerp rushes out

Percy Indeed, I was, until that moment, unaware that a mere donkey was
capable of such speed ... Out of the garden we galloped, across a meadow
and then with barely a second's pause, into the deepest part of the forest ...

The donkey brays triumphantly

Paul Whooa! Whooa! Whooa! Where are we going? Where are you taking me, you brute?
Percy By way of reply the donkey merely brayed louder and increased the pace of its gallop. It was as if the beast was enchanted. On and on we strode and just as I had given up all hope of ever stopping again ...

The donkey gives a final bray and rears up, hurling Paul on to the ground where he lies. The donkey, too, collapses nearby

Paul (*as he falls*) Aaaah!
Percy How long I lay unconscious I do not know. When I awoke it was dark ...

The Lights dim

Leonora, Yerp and Mrs Yerp enter with lanterns

Leonora Thank God, he's still alive ...
Mrs Yerp The snow broke his fall, else he'd be a dead 'un.
Leonora Find my brother. Yerp, we must find my brother. He cannot be far away ... (*Calling*) Frederick! Frederick!
Yerp (*moving off slightly*) Mr Stringer, sir! Mr Stringer!

Paul groans

Leonora Rupert ...
Percy For the second time in twenty-four hours, I was to awaken to the sight of this angel of mercy.
Paul Leonora, I ——
Leonora No, don't try to stand, Rupert. You've had a bad fall.
Yerp (*calling*) He's over here, ma'am. Over here.
Leonora Is he all right?
Yerp Yes, ma'am. He's still breathing.
Leonora Oh, thank God.
Mrs Yerp The Lord be praised.

Leonora moves to Frederick

Percy I wondered for a moment why there should be so much relief and divine gratitude at the survival of what appeared to me to be an extremely foul-tempered, headstrong donkey. I am, of course, not insensitive myself to our dumb friends but for this particular creature I was fully prepared to make an exception. Imagine my astonishment then, when I saw that the creature around whom they were all anxiously gathered was no donkey but rather the body of my unsociable host of the previous evening, Frederick Stringer.

Frederick I'm all right. I'm perfectly all right. Leave me alone, I tell you.

Leonora Frederick ——

Frederick (*sharply*) I said leave me!

Percy His temper seemed not to have improved one iota.

Paul (*staggering to his feet*) Mr Stringer — how do you come to be here as well?

Leonora It's all right, Rupert. It is not your concern.

Paul But I demand to know. How is it that he is here like myself, injured in the snow? You must tell me. Leonora! I demand to know.

Percy But to this day, no satisfactory answer was I ever to receive. How Frederick came to be lying near me in the snow and what became of that extraordinary donkey will I fear remain a mystery, ladies and gentlemen, for ever more.

Percy appears to have finished his story. He marks the end of his story rather dramatically with a slight pause. The keyboard player plays a final flourish

Paul Is that it, then?

Percy Yes.

Paul Not much of an ending.

Leonora It never is.

All (*gloomily*) No ...

Percy What are you complaining about? It's a mystery story. It's a classic Victorian mystery story.

Paul You might at least solve the mystery.

Percy If I did that it wouldn't be a mystery story, would it?

Paul What are you talking about? There's plenty of mystery stories where the mystery gets solved — Sherlock Holmes. He solves his mysteries.

Leonora Yes, Hercule Poirot ——

Yerp — Inspector Morse ——

Mrs Yerp — Columbo ——

Percy (*angrily*) Well, it doesn't get solved in this one, so there. That's it! Enough. The end of my very own story. Finish. Goodbye. Thank you very much. Hope you've enjoyed it. Come back next week. I'll have my props back, and all. (*He starts gathering up his belongings*)

As soon as Percy starts collecting his things, Peter appears; we hear his voice before we see him

Peter (*as he enters*) Chapter Two. The Mystery of Deepwood is revealed. Just as I had given up all hope of learning the secret of Deepwood House, Frederick stepped forward with a cry ——
Percy Just a minute.
Peter What?
Percy What are you doing?
Peter Telling the rest of the story.
Percy You can't do that.
Peter Why not?
Percy It's ended. I finished it.
Peter You may have finished it, I haven't. I'm carrying on.
Percy You can't do that. It's my story.
Peter It was your story. It's not any more. You just said, you've finished with it. You've thrown it away. He just said that, didn't he? Didn't he just say that?
All Yes.
Peter There you are, they agree with me. Goodbye. Nice to have seen you.
Percy This is illegal. This is unlawful. You can't do this.
Peter Just watch me ——
Percy (*going off*) You haven't heard the end of this, you know. You haven't seen the last of me.
Peter Bye!
All (*except Peter*) Bye!

Percy exits, leaving his props

Peter To continue. Chapter Two. The Mystery of Deepwood is revealed. Just as I had given up all hope of learning the secret of Deepwood House, Frederick stepped forward with a cry ——
Frederick It's no use, Leonora. We cannot conceal this secret a moment longer. He must be told the truth, he deserves that at least.
Leonora But Frederick ...
Frederick Leonora, but for the snow, Mr Fellowes would be surely dead. Since by some miracle he has been spared, he should be rewarded at the very least with the truth ... Are you strong enough to walk, my friend?
Paul Yes, I think so ...
Leonora Here, take my arm, Rupert ...
Paul Thank you, Leonora ...
Peter And thus we made our way slowly back to the house, Yerp leading the

way, followed by the three of us — Mr Fellowes, our uninvited guest, my loyal, loving sister Leonora, myself, Frederick Stringer — and finally Mrs Yerp bringing up the rear. Throughout our walk back I observed our guest relying greatly on the support of my sister's arm — though I suspect if truth be told the support was more spiritual and emotional than physical. For it did not take one of much perception to deduce that the two were clearly in love. Alas, as things were at present, their love was a fruitless and futile thing. As we walked, I tried to explain to Mr Fellowes the nature of the curse that had been brought upon our family — that I had brought upon our family, for in all this it cannot be emphasized too strongly that my dear, precious, sweet-natured sister was entirely innocent.

Frederick Mr Fellowes, I would have you know, sir, that I am to blame for all that has happened here. Many years ago, I behaved foolishly. I was punished quite rightly for this behaviour. My punishment continues to this day. Over twenty years. Twenty years. Will it ever end ...?

Leonora Frederick ——

Frederick It's all right, my dear. The simple fact is, Mr Fellowes, that due to some spell that has been put upon me, by day, during the hours of daylight I am transformed into the creature you saw earlier and — tried to ride ...

Paul The donkey. *You* were the donkey? Is this possible?

Frederick It is not only possible, Mr Fellowes, it is the truth. By night, I resume my normal shape as you see me now. Though my appetites, alas, remain those of a beast. And by day ... I am, as you witnessed me — that — thing in the field.

Paul How did this occur? Who could possibly have done this heartless thing to you? And why?

Frederick (*shaking his head*) It is a long story. I couldn't ——

Leonora The tragedy is, Rupert, that even as a donkey, my brother is unable to enjoy himself or give innocent pleasure to others. As you yourself discovered, he is a creature that none may ride or even stroke.

Frederick No sooner are they upon my back than all the fires of hell burn through me. I must shake them from me and kill them or perish myself.

Paul Even a child may not ride you ——?

Leonora No man, woman or child.

Frederick Save one.

Leonora (*softly*) Save one.

Yerp Do you want to stop for thistles, Mr Frederick?

Frederick No Yerp, no. Not now, let us go on.

Paul You mention there is one who alone can ride you. Who is this man?

Frederick It is no man but a woman, Mr Fellowes. It is none other than the woman I betrayed.

Paul And is it she who put this spell upon you?

Frederick No. It was not she.

Paul Then who? I am acutely curious to know, Mr Stringer.

Frederick It is a sad and complicated tale but if you so wish, I will tell you ...

Leonora Frederick, is this wise, my dear?

Frederick (*shaking his head, sadly*) Where is the harm now, Leonora, where is the harm?

During the following, the group make their way off

Peter And as we walked through the snow, retracing our tracks back to the house, I, Frederick Stringer, told him my story — my very own story. And that story — which I shall entitle, *The Enchanted Suitor* — I shall relate to you, ladies and gentlemen, should you be good enough to return in a few moments' time. We shall expect you. Please, do not be tardy.

He bows and goes off

CURTAIN

ACT II

The same

The Deepwood House furniture, etc., has been removed. There are chairs on stage which are used variously throughout the act. Some of the props are set in Peter, Paul and Percy's prop cases

Peter enters

Peter And now, ladies and gentlemen, my very own story — a tale of contemporary times that I have entitled *The Enchanted Suitor*, being the sad cautionary account of one Frederick Stringer, landowner and part-time donkey. When he was younger, twenty years younger than he was in our last story, Frederick was really a very handsome, extremely good-looking young man.

Percy comes on as Frederick when young. He smiles around him

He had only to step outside his door for young — hey!
Percy Carry on.
Peter What are you doing back here?
Percy Young Frederick, what else?
Peter You can't do young Frederick.
Percy Why not? They said I could.
Peter Who said you could?
Percy Them back there. That lot. They knew you wanted a handsome bloke. They took a vote. I won hands down.
Peter Where's the real young Frederick?
Percy Playing cards.
Peter This is disgraceful.
Percy Carry on. I'm ready.
Peter (*muttering*) This is *my* very own story. You're not my idea of young Frederick.
Percy Come on, carry on. Frederick was really a very handsome, extremely good-looking young man ...
Peter ... he was also unfortunately extremely conceited. He had only to step outside his door for young women practically to swoon away at the sight of him.

As he speaks two young women enter, walk past Percy and nearly faint with excitement

Percy preens himself

The women exit

The problem with young Frederick was — like a number of very, very good-looking people — he didn't really have much time for other folk at all. The only person he really loved was himself. His greatest pleasure was to stand in front of the mirror.

Percy (*standing in front of a "mirror", admiringly*) Oh! Oh, you devil. You dashing devil, you! Mmm. Mmm.

Peter So, although many girls fell in love with him ...

One of the young women returns and gazes adoringly at Percy

He had no time for them, however beautiful they might be ...

Percy Shoo! Shoo! Go away, woman!

The woman runs off, wailing

Wretched thing!

Peter He was extremely thoughtless and insensitive. And as for plain women ...

A plain woman enters

He had no time for them at all ...

Percy Uurrgggh!

The plain woman exits, weeping

Peter In fact, there was very little to be said in Frederick's defence except that he was young and had been born naturally handsome and gifted and therefore probably didn't know any better. But he was soon to learn. For Frederick, although he didn't yet know it, was about to fall in love. Hopelessly in love. It started like most love stories — completely by accident ...

Cecilia enters. She is carrying some tiny parcels. She fails to see Percy

They collide

Cecilia Oh!
Percy Whoops!
Cecilia I'm so sorry ——
Percy No, *I'm* sorry ——
Cecilia No, it was my fault ——
Percy No, it was *my* fault ——

They catch sight of each other and move away as they speak

Percy }
Cecilia } (*together*) No, it was very definitely ... my ... fault ...

They stare at each other without moving

Music

Peter Now for Frederick, having a stranger staring adoringly at him like this was no new experience. But to undergo the same emotion himself — here was a novelty.
Percy I'm — I'm ... I'm Frederick Stringer.
Cecilia How do you do? I'm ... I'm Cecilia Butterworth.
Percy (*dreamily*) Hallo.
Cecilia (*dreamily*) Hallo. Frederick Stinger ...
Percy Stringer.
Cecilia Stringer. Sorry.
Percy That's quite all right, Miss Butterscotch.
Cecilia Worth. Butterworth.
Percy I'm sorry. Will you ever forgive me?
Cecilia Of course. Of course, of course, of course ...
Peter And they went on like that in similar vein for a very long time but we won't bother with all that now because unless you happen to be in love yourself it does tend to get a bit boring. So, anyway, Frederick walked Cecilia Butterworth home and very generously offered to carry all her extremely heavy parcels.
Cecilia (*admiringly*) You're so strong!

Percy laughs carelessly

Peter When they reached her house, number forty-nine Hollyhock Street, to show how grateful she was to him, Cecilia invited Frederick inside for a cup of tea. It was a delightful little semi-detached house, tastefully furnished and as clean and neat as a new pin. Frederick thoroughly approved.

Cecilia Mummy!

Peter ... cried Cecilia.

Cecilia I'm home!

Alicia hurries on

Alicia Darling, I wondered where on earth you'd — (*seeing Frederick*) Oh.

Percy Hallo.

Cecilia I've brought someone home.

Alicia Oh, yes. How lovely. Mr —— ?

Percy Stringer. Frederick Stringer.

Cecilia Mr Stringer picked me up, Mummy. After I'd fallen over.

Alicia Oh, how simply sweet of him.

Cecilia I dropped all my parcels but he picked them up too.

Alicia Lovely.

Cecilia And then he carried them home.

Alicia Super. Would you like some tea, Mr String?

Percy Stringer ——

Alicia Sorry.

Percy Yes please, if it's no trouble, Mrs Buttermere ——

Alicia Butterworth.

Percy Yes, sorry.

Alicia Do sit down.

Percy Thank you.

Alicia Darling, keep Mr Stringer entertained. Perhaps you could show him your pictures.

Cecilia Oh, Mummy, he doesn't want to see those.

Alicia I'm sure he'd adore to see them.

Cecilia No, no, no, no.

Alicia Do you care for pictures at all, Mr Stringer?

Percy Pictures? What sort of pictures are these?

Alicia Little pictures. She draws them herself. She's really frightfully talented, everybody says so. But she's unbelievably modest. I keep telling her she's got to push herself more. You need to push yourself, darling.

Cecilia Oh, Mummy.

Alicia You tell her to push herself, Mr Stringer.

Percy I will, I will.

Alicia Won't be a tick.

Alicia exits

Percy What a charming mother you have.

Cecilia Oh gosh, heavens, gollyhoppers, she's ghastly. She's so embarrassing sometimes ...

Percy Rubbish. I bet your father's amazing as well, isn't he?

Cecilia No, Daddy's — Daddy's gone. He's no longer with us.

Percy Oh, I'm sorry. Did he die recently?

Cecilia No, he's not dead, he just — he just doesn't live here any more. He's gone off. He got — well, I think he got a bit cheesed off with us really and he sort of took off.

Percy How frightful for you.

Cecilia Yes, it was a bit. It was worse for Mummy, of course.

Percy Just the two of you then now, is there?

Cecilia Well, and Em of course.

Percy Em?

Cecilia My sister Em. Short for Emilia. I expect you'll meet her. She's a super person, you'll love her. Very warm and friendly. Look, you don't really want to see my pictures, do you?

Percy Of course.

Cecilia Oh, but they're terrible, they're awful, they're ghastly, they're absolutely blush-making.

Percy I bet they're not. Come on, don't be so modest. Push yourself.

Cecilia (*needing no second invitation*) OK, I'll go and get them. Wait there. (*As she goes*) Look out of the window if you want to. Feel free.

She dashes out

Percy Thank you.

Peter Left alone in the front room, Frederick took advantage of Cecilia's offer and looked out of the window. He saw a neat little garden, with a tidy little lawn and a trim little fence. There were some smart little flowers standing in spruce-like rows, and some clean, orderly, just a little tiny bit but not all *that* much crazy paving.

Percy How absolutely lovely.

Emilia enters

Peter So absorbed was he with the view that Frederick failed to notice someone entering the room. It was Cecilia's sister, Emilia. Emilia, as Cecilia had intimated earlier, was the warmest and friendliest person you could possibly hope to meet. She was also one of the plainest.

Emilia Hallo, there.

Peter Frederick turned to see who it was. As I have told you, lack of beauty in others affected him deeply. He reacted to the sight of the poor girl with his characteristic sensitivity.

Percy Uurrgghh!

Emilia Oh!

Percy Sorry.

Emilia That's all right. I'm — it's always happening. You're a friend of Cecilia's, I presume. Hallo, I'm her sister, Emilia.

Percy (*hardly looking at her*) Hallo, I'm Frederick. It's awfully good to meet you. I've heard so much about you.

Emilia I expect you've been hearing how warm and friendly I am.

Percy Yes, yes, I have. You bet.

Emilia Yes I thought you might somehow. I also dance, you know. Classical, modern and tap.

Percy How clever.

Emilia Waste of time, really. Nobody ever wants to watch me do it.

Percy What a shame. I would.

Emilia You wouldn't, you know. You say you would but if I started dancing for you now, you'd just stare at your feet or at the floor.

Peter Frederick, though, was anxious not to antagonize the sister of the girl he had secretly already decided to marry.

Percy I bet I wouldn't, you know. I'd love to see you dance. Really I would.

Emilia Really? OK. You asked for it. Classical, modern or tap?

Percy Well. Bit of each would be nice.

Emilia OK. Here goes. Hold on to your hat. A-one, a-two ...

The keyboard player strikes up. Emilia starts to dance for Percy. He stares at her for a second, then hurriedly at the floor

Peter (*as Emilia dances*) Poor Frederick became fearfully embarrassed. Not only was the poor girl distressingly unattractive to look at but she danced like a baby hippo. Fortunately, rescue was at hand ...

Alicia enters with a small tea table and tea things

Alicia (*sharply*) Emilia, stop that immediately.

The music stops. So does Emilia. She looks embarrassed

That's better. Now sit down at once and stop showing off. You're embarrassing everyone.

Emilia (*softly*) Yes, Mummy. (*She sits apart from them, her head hung low*)

Alicia I'm afraid Emilia here is a dreadful show-off, Mr Stringer. I hope you weren't too dreadfully embarrassed.

Percy Not at all, Mrs Butterworth. I was thoroughly entertained. Thank you, Emilia.

Emilia flashes him a quick smile of gratitude

Alicia (*drily*) Really? One lump or two?

Percy Two, thank you.

Alicia Hand round the tea, Emilia. Do something useful with your life for heaven's sake.

Emilia Yes, Mummy. (*She hands round the tea awkwardly*)

Alicia Emilia rather fancies herself as a dancer, Mr Stringer, but I can't say I'd give much for her chances with the Royal Ballet, would you? (*She laughs*)

Percy (*embarrassed*) I — I ... I really wouldn't know ——

Alicia Well, I'm not an expert but I'm sure there must be some upper limit on the size of feet for a start, don't you think? Careful, darling, don't spill it ...

Emilia Sorry, Mummy ——

Alicia She's unbelievably clumsy. I don't know where she gets this clumsiness from either, I'm sure.

Cecilia enters with her "portfolio"

Cecilia Hallo. Sorry, everyone ...

Alicia Oh, come in, darling, you're just in time for tea.

Cecilia Super. Hi, Em ...

Emilia Hallo.

Cecilia You've met Frederick?

Emilia Yes.

Alicia Em's been keeping him entertained. In her inimitable manner.

Cecilia Oh. Sorry I took so long. I couldn't decide which ones to show you so I've brought down the lot.

Alicia What does it matter, they're all equally good. I don't think I could choose my favourite even if you forced me. Emilia, pass this to your sister. Come along.

Emilia dutifully passes the cup to Cecilia who places it on the floor beside her. Cecilia proceeds to open her portfolio of dull watercolours. Emilia resumes her seat in the corner. Alicia swells with pride. Percy tries to enthuse

Now, Mr Stringer, tell me what you think of these. Be honest, you can be perfectly honest, can't he Cecilia?

Cecilia Oh don't, please, no don't. Most of these are just dreadful, I know they are.

Peter In fact, Cecilia was wrong in only one respect. All the pictures were equally dreadful. Frederick was no art expert but even he could tell at half a glance that the woman he loved, the girl he would willing lay down his life for, had about as much artistic talent as a disoriented snail. And yet, love being what it is ...

Percy Oh, oh, oh, oh. Oh. Now, these are quite extraordinary. What a unique talent!

Alicia Now, what did I say ——

Cecilia Oh ——

Percy Absolutely remarkable. So fresh. So untouched by the taint of commercialism ——

Alicia Yes, yes, yes ——

Percy —— unencumbered by dull formal training or the rigid restraints of technique. Yours is a true, innate talent, Cecilia.

Cecilia (*modestly*) Thank you.

Alicia There, Cecilia, listen to that. That's someone who knows about these things.

Percy Oh, please, I really know nothing ...

Alicia Enough to recognize talent.

Percy Oh, yes. Enough to recognize that, I trust.

During the following, Alicia and Emilia exit. Alicia takes the tea things, Emilia takes the portfolio

Peter And at last Frederick took his leave of the family, reflecting that he would probably in time grow to love Cecilia's pictures, who knows? And if not he would never, he was certain, ever grow tired of her glorious face. Over the next few days, Frederick and Cecilia spent every hour they could together, celebrating and cementing their new-found love.

Music

Frederick and Cecilia dash hither and thither being terribly happy together

Less than a month later, one summer's evening, Frederick plucked up the courage to ask Cecilia to be his wife. He had seldom been so happy, never so in love with another. Why, whole days passed without him looking in a mirror at all. It had to be the real thing. Cecilia, needless to say, said yes.

Alicia enters, followed by Emilia at a distance

They broke the news to her mother who was overjoyed. In fact, everyone was happy. Or nearly everyone. As usual, nobody noticed Emilia; the plain, clumsy, talentless good-hearted Emilia, as usual, was ignored. Preparations for the wedding were soon underway. All mothers love weddings and Alicia loved them more than most mothers.

A great deal of rushing about with parcels and fabrics, etc.

Two days before the big day, something rather odd occurred. Frederick had popped round to their house to deliver some particular paper doilies that Alicia had asked him to collect. Cecilia was out somewhere, probably at the hairdressers. She had already spent several days in the hairdressers recently for she wanted to look just right for her walk down the aisle. When Frederick arrived though, Alicia seemed in an unusually solemn and serious mood. She asked Frederick if she could have a word with him alone in the front room.

Percy Of course. What's it about? Nothing serious, I hope?
Peter It seemed, frankly, a little late to ask if his intentions were honourable.
Alicia Sit down, Frederick. I want to say something to you.
Percy Yes, Alicia?
Alicia The point is — I don't want Cecilia to be hurt. Ever.
Percy Hurt?
Alicia You're positive you love her?
Percy Of course!
Alicia You'll always love her and care for her?
Percy How can you doubt that?
Alicia I'm sorry. I have a — I have a reason.
Percy Something to do with me? Something I've said? Something I've done?
Alicia Oh, no ... I'm sure you mean what you say. It's only ... It's just, Frederick, that people sometimes turn out differently from how you expect, that's all. You see?
Percy How do you mean?
Alicia They just do. You marry them and then you turn round and they're different. I can't really explain it.
Percy I don't see this at all. What are you trying to tell me?
Alicia You're sure you wouldn't be happier with, say, Emilia?
Percy (*appalled*) Emilia?

Alicia Yes.

Percy Absolutely not. Me and Emilia? Emilia and me? Certainly not. That would be quite ... I mean, she has a marvellous warm and friendly nature, I know, but I could never love her. I love Cecilia. She's the most beautiful creature in the world.

Alicia Whereas Emilia isn't.

Percy Well, frankly no. She has this lovely nature but ——

Alicia Yes. Well, I can say no more then, Frederick. Nothing I can do will make you reconsider.

Percy You want me to reconsider?

Alicia I want you to be certain. Because I'm not sure you're going to be happy with Cecilia, Frederick. I have this dreadful foreboding.

Percy Nonsense. (*He stares at her*) There's something else, isn't there? Something you haven't told me, Alicia? What is it?

Alicia Nothing. At least, nothing that any one of us can do a thing about, I'm afraid. (*She kisses him suddenly on the forehead*) Take care of yourself, Frederick, I beg you. I'm really dreadfully fond of you, you see. (*Breaking from him, a little overcome*) Excuse me. I must unpack the confetti.

She hurries out

Percy stands bewildered

Percy What on earth did she mean by all that?

Peter Frederick was deeply puzzled. What *could* she have meant? Marry Emilia instead? What a suggestion: Why, he could barely bring himself to look at the poor girl. Whereas Cecilia — he could gaze upon her for ever. And just think, the day after tomorrow he would be able to do so. Till death them did part. Oh, happy man!

The following is acted out as Peter narrates

Alicia, Emilia and Cecilia enter

And soon enough, all doubts put firmly aside, the wedding day came. The sun shone brightly on the couple. The bride looked perfect — her hair just right. Even Emilia, the bridesmaid, managed to look — well, almost presentable — though she did trip over once or twice.

Alicia and Emilia exit

Then on to the honeymoon, a perfect, love-filled, sun-drenched honeymoon. No second thoughts so far. And so back to their own little house, number forty-one Hollyhock Street, just four doors down from the in-laws.

Cecilia exits

A few weeks later, Frederick was standing in his front room gazing out of his window. He tended to gaze out of his window quite a lot these days. Mainly to avoid looking too much at the walls of their home, every inch of which were covered by his wife's watercolour pictures. Frederick was learning to live with them but they were, he had to confess, an acquired taste. One that he had not personally yet acquired. So he gazed as usual out of his window, noting with some pride his neat little garden, with its tidy little lawn and its trim little fence. He derived some pleasure in observing their smart little flowers standing in spruce-like little rows, and their clean, orderly, just a little tiny bit but not all *that* much, crazy paving.

Cecilia pokes her head round the door

Cecilia Supper's ready, darling.
Percy (*thoughtfully*) Righto, darling.

He turns to her

(*Startled*) Ah!
Cecilia What is it, darling?
Percy Nothing. You've done something new to your hair, have you, darling?
Cecilia No.
Percy To your make-up?
Cecilia No.
Percy Something's different.
Cecilia No, darling. Silly. Come on. It's on the table.

She exits

Peter But as Frederick made to follow her, he felt rather peculiar. Could it be that his wife was growing — less attractive? Surely not. She was, after all, the most beautiful woman in the world — and yet ... Something about her was — just for a second — was almost *un*attractive. No. He was imagining things. He was losing touch with reality. He looked out of his window again to reassure himself that all was well. And at that moment, he saw someone passing in the street. A woman, faintly familiar. And yet quite unfamiliar, for this was someone — for a recently married man at least — disquietingly attractive. Just for a second, that was.

Emilia enters and walks past, then exits

For then as she turned and saw him watching her she smiled at him. A warm and thoroughly friendly smile. And he saw at once it was Emilia. Plain old, clumsy old Emilia. Warm and friendly, maybe, but ... not beautiful. Never. Attractive perhaps in — certain lights, but compared with Cecilia ... What nonsense!

Percy shakes his head and smiles

But as the weeks went by, as regards his wife, the feeling wouldn't quite go away. In fact some days she looked positively ugly.

Cecilia enters, scowling

Cecilia Look, darling, are you going to fix it or not?
Percy Yes, I'm just coming, darling.
Cecilia Well, it's leaking all over the place, darling. I thought you said you were going to fix it.
Percy I will, I will, darling. I've only just got home from work, you know ...
Cecilia (*flouncing out*) Well, it's all right for some then, isn't it?

She exits, and re-enters during the following with a book and sewing kit. The narration is acted out

Peter But then, these little tiffs are common enough in any marriage and soon pass. And Frederick continued to work hard and saved what money he could for that magic day when they would start a family. And Cecilia worked hard to keep the place nice for them, thinking up little improvements to make their little home even prettier. And she and Frederick had even decorated the spare bedroom as a nursery for the child they fully expected to start any day now.

Percy and Cecilia sit apart. She is sewing. He is reading. They both seem very unhappy. The clock strikes

The only major problem to all this was that, after a year of marriage, Frederick could no longer bear to look at Cecilia at all. She had grown most unbelievably plain. And as you recall, the one thing that Frederick could not abide was plain people. In fact, looking in the mirror of late, he detected a certain diminishing in his own good looks. No, impossible.

Percy (*rising*) Well, I'll — I'll be off to bed then, dear.

Cecilia (*coolly*) All right, dear.

Percy Are you coming up, dear?

Cecilia Not quite yet, dear.

Peter Thank heavens for that, thought Frederick.

Percy Righty-ho ...

Peter ... said Frederick, rather too cheerfully.

Percy Night-night, then.

Cecilia I see.

Percy What?

Cecilia No, nothing.

Percy What is it?

Cecilia Not even a good-night kiss now, I notice.

Percy Oh, no, right. Here you are.

Cecilia (*pushing him away*) No, I don't want one now. It's no good now, is it?

Percy Come on, come on. Don't be silly, dear.

Cecilia No, I don't want you slobbering all over me. Go away, go away ...

Percy What on earth's got into you? You're impossible these days ——

Cecilia (*hysterically*) Don't you start telling me I'm impossible — you're the one who's impossible, not me. You're the one who can't even bear to look at me. Who can't even bring himself to kiss me unless I beg him to. You're the one. I can't help it if you don't find me attractive. Don't blame me, it's not my fault, is it? I knew this would happen, I knew it would, they all said it would ...

She rushes out, weeping bitterly. Percy stands amazed

Peter Poor Frederick was quite staggered at this sudden outburst.

Percy Good Lord.

Peter Partly because he had had no appreciation of how clearly he had allowed his real feelings to show.

Percy Heavens!

Peter He decided the best thing was to go for a walk. Allow his wife time to cool down. Poor Frederick was quite unaware that so far as cooling down was concerned, women invariably took far longer to do so than men. It was a bright moonlit evening and Frederick set off along the street intending to walk around the local park. That very park where a year ago he had walked and talked and dreamed with Cecilia.

Emilia enters

Ah me! But he had gone less than a few hundred yards when he spied coming towards him an apparition of such beauty, such grace, such divine enchantment, that he stopped dead in his tracks.

Percy stops dead and stares at Emilia

Who could she be, this vision of loveliness?

Emilia Oh, hallo, Frederick.

Percy (*amazed*) Emilia.

Peter Frederick at that moment fell in love all over again.

Emilia What are you doing out at this hour?

Peter The moonlight picking out the soft, gentle contours of her face, sparkling in her hair like spun moonbeams ...

Emilia Frederick?

Peter Her eyes so clear and bright, brimful of warmth and friendliness ...

Emilia Frederick, are you all right?

Percy (*hoarsely*) Yes.

Emilia Are you sure? You look terrible. Here, come inside for a minute. I've just come back from my evening down at the mission. Come on, take my arm ...

Peter Not only warm and friendly and beautiful but she worked for the poor ... Oh, perfection. She led Frederick into the house.

Emilia Mummy's out at the moment. Sit down. Would you like some tea? I'll make us a pot.

Percy No, no ... I'll ... be fine ...

Emilia Shall I pop round and fetch Cecilia? Is she at home?

Percy Yes, she is. But no. Don't bother. I'll be fine. Please, Em. Sit down.

Emilia Sure?

Percy Please.

Emilia Right. (*She sits*)

A pause. Percy stares at her

What on earth are you staring at?

Percy Would you — would you do something for me?

Emilia Of course. What is it?

Percy Would you — would you dance for me, Emilia?

Emilia Dance?

Percy Yes.

Emilia For you?

Percy Please.

Emilia But I'm awful. Everybody says I'm awful. I can't dance. I've no
talent.

Percy I think you have. (*Pause*) Please.

Emilia Well, all right. If you're sure. If it'll make you feel better. (*She rises*)
Classical, modern or tap.

Percy I really don't mind. Anything. I just want to watch you — moving.

Emilia Well, OK. It'd better be classical then. It's a bit quieter. It's getting
rather late.

*The keyboard player plays something soft and romantic. Emilia moves and
sways gently. Percy watches her*

Peter And as he watched her, Frederick was suddenly gripped with a
compulsion to dance with her — even though Frederick had never before
danced classical ballet in his entire life, the urge to partner Emilia became
irresistible ...

*Percy and Emilia dance for a second or two together. At the finish they
embrace and kiss. They freeze thus under the next*

But Frederick, as he embraced his sister-in-law in the front room of his
mother-in-law's house, had overlooked another vital fact concerning
women in general and wives in particular. That when their lives become
difficult or their marriages impossible they invariably run home to mother.

*Cecilia enters with a small suitcase. She seems Emilia and Percy and
screams. The lovers part hastily*

Cecilia (*flinging down her case, beside herself with fury*) I knew it. I knew
this would happen. You — you little hussy ...

Emilia Cecilia ...

Percy Cecilia, I'm sorry, I ——

Cecilia I knew you'd do this. I knew you would. Mummy said you would
and you've done it! I'll never forgive you for this. Never!

She rushes from the room. Alicia enters and passes her as she leaves

Emilia Cecilia ...! Oh heavens. Oh Lord. Oh gosh.

Emilia runs out after her sister, taking the case with her

Percy smiles lamely at Alicia

Alicia (*shaking her head*) Oh dear.

Percy I've ruined everything now, haven't I?

Alicia I'm afraid you have rather.

Percy Burnt my boats.

Alicia Completely.

Percy Both boats.

Alicia You've sunk the entire navy, Frederick.

Percy (*sitting down*) Oh. How can anyone be so stupid? What a fool I am! What a fool!

Peter And Alicia, though she did not bother to contradict him, at least had the decency not to say, I told you so. Though she had every excuse to do so. And the moral of the story is this. Before you marry anyone, not only examine them very, very closely but do make sure you examine yourself as well. That is if you don't want to make a complete and utter ass of yourself.

Percy starts braying like a donkey. The keyboard plays a flourish

During the following Paul enters, unobserved by the others

Percy Is that it?

Peter That's it.

Percy That's not much of an ending.

Peter What do you mean?

Percy You complained about my ending, this one's much worse. No ending at all.

Peter It's a perfectly good story. It's a simple, modern morality tale, that's all.

Percy You might at least finish it.

Alicia Yes, I think you ought to finish it.

Peter It is finished! Look, I'm not arguing. That's my very own story and that's it. It's finished. Thank you very much, ladies and gentlemen, hope you enjoyed it. Goodbye and thank you.

Paul takes up the narrative

Paul Chapter Three. The true story of the Butterworth Family. Frederick turned to Alicia. Only she could tell him how to extricate himself from his plight ——

Peter Just a minute.

Paul What?

Peter What are you doing?

Paul Telling the rest of the story.

Peter You can't do that.

Paul Why not?

Peter I've just said. It's ended. It's finished.

Paul You may have finished it, I haven't. I'm carrying on.

Peter You can't do that. It's my story.

Paul It was your story. It's not any more. You've finished with it. Anyway, you carried on his story. Why shouldn't I carry on yours? Fair's fair, isn't it?

All Yes.

Paul There you are, they agree with me. Goodbye. Nice to have seen you.

Peter This is disgraceful. You can't do this.

Paul Here I go ...

Peter (*going off*) You haven't heard the end of this, you know. You haven't seen the last of me.

Paul Bye!

All Bye!

Peter exits, leaving his props

Paul And Frederick turned to Alicia and begged her to tell him how all this had befallen him. For he knew that with her surely, lay the secret.

Alicia All right, I'll tell you.

Paul ... said Alicia.

Alicia If truth be told the fault does lie with me.

Paul And her eyes filled with tears as she began to speak. And so begins my very own story, a fantastical magical tale of long, long ago which I shall entitle *The Sorcerer's Daughters*.

Alicia Many years ago, Frederick, when I was much younger — about the age my daughters are now — I was a very pretty little thing — is that hard for you to imagine, Frederick?

Percy No, not at all.

Paul ... cried Frederick gallantly, if a little untruthfully.

Alicia I suppose I looked rather like Cecilia does today.

Cecilia comes on as the young Alicia

And in due course I fell in love as one does and married the most handsome of men — not unlike you, Frederick ——

Percy Thank you.

Alicia — or as you used to be. But this man was not only handsome and rich, he was also a sorcerer.

Percy A sorcerer?

Peter enters during the following dressed as Varius. He is hooded in a wizard's cloak

Alicia Yes, you smile, but it's true. Such people do exist. Though they're very secretive and unless you marry them you'd never find out that they were one.

Peter moves to Cecilia, who runs to greet him

His name was Varius and he was a white wizard. His spells were always for the good. Including the spell he cast upon me when we first met. Oh, we were so happy, you cannot imagine, Frederick ... He was the most remarkable of men ...

At this point Peter throws back the hood to reveal his true identity. He is about to kiss Cecilia when Paul interrupts

Paul Oh, no ...
Peter Fair's fair ... They said I could back there. They've got to a very exciting point in their card game.
Paul All right, carry on. (*Muttering*) Anyone less like a sorcerer.
Cecilia Looks all right to me.
Alicia Better than the one out there ...
Cecilia Much ——
Paul Get on with it ...
Alicia He was the most remarkable of men and ours was truly the happiest of marriages. It was not, as I say, until we did marry that I realized that my husband had magical powers. But since he used those powers only for good and never to harm anyone — that made me all the happier. And in a year or two, I presented him with two daughters ——

Cecilia presents Peter with two baby-like bundles (from one of the prop cases)

During the following Peter and Cecilia exit with the babies, delighted

— whom we christened Cecilia and Emilia.
Paul And young Frederick listened spellbound as Alicia continued to relate her story.

During the following, Alicia and Percy exit

Because they were so rich they lived in this huge castle where the children played happily all day long. For they both had the run of the place — all except for one room which no-one was allowed to enter, not even their mother. This was the room where the sorcerer, Varius, kept his spells and potions — a secret room only he and he alone could enter. The sorcerer's code is a strict one — for if anyone other than they themselves found out their secrets, then the penalties laid down by the Imperial Grand Society of Sorcerers were too terrible to mention.

Cecilia and Emilia enter during the following, playing with a ball

And Cecilia and Emilia grew up to be beautiful and strong and healthy — Cecilia favouring her mother's looks and Emilia her father's.

Alicia, now as herself, enters with Peter. They watch their children proudly

And Alicia and Varius were the proudest parents there ever could have been.

Peter watches for a second and then exits

If there was single cloud in the sky, it was this. Alicia was a most ambitious mother. She wanted not just beautiful children, but the most beautiful children in the whole world. And she wanted them, eventually, not to marry ordinary, decent, honest men but the richest, most handsome princes in the kingdom.

A village boy enters and ogles the girls as they play

And if an unsuitable boy should even approach them ...

One of the girls drops the ball. The village boy picks it up and holds it out for them to come and retrieve

She would quickly shoo them away.

Alicia shouts at the village boy

The village boy drops the ball and runs off

During the following Alicia beckons her daughters over to her and re-proaches them

And she would reprimand her children most severely for talking with common, rough boys. And both being children who loved and trusted their mother, they believed her and so the next time a common, rough boy dared to come near them ——

The village boy reappears. The girls shoo him off

Alicia looks on approvingly. They act according to the following narration. (The props, etc., are obtained from the prop cases)

—— neither girl would have anything whatever to do with him. Of course, their father knew nothing of this, but if he had done he would have been very angry but maybe, just maybe, he might have stopped all the dreadful things that were about to happen. In due course, the girls grew up and put aside childish games and became mature, beautiful, sophisticated young women. What parent could have asked for more? Alicia, the proudest of mothers, doted on her girls. She adored them. Their every wish was her command. They were, if truth be told, terribly, terribly spoilt. And yet, beautiful as they were, Alicia felt that somehow they could be still more beautiful. Tall as they were, wouldn't it be lovely if they were just a mite taller? A fraction more elegant? A tiny bit more charming? Surely her husband could arrange that? A couple of quick spells. After all, he'd cured them of measles, hadn't he? But Varius refused and said no, magic wasn't to be used for personal gain and certainly not for foolish things like that. The girls were quite beautiful enough and they should thank their lucky stars and be content with the way they were. In fact, he got quite firm with her. So she had to pretend to make the best of it. Because although it happened very rarely, if her husband ever did lose his temper, it was a terrible thing to behold and it often rained for weeks afterwards. And then, one day, Varius had to go away for a while to attend the Society of Sorcerers' Annual Conference up north. He bade his family farewell and told them to take good care, he'd only be gone a week or so. And off he went. That same evening when both the girls were in bed, Alicia began to think. What would be the harm, she thought, in using just a tiny spell? If it helped her daughters? After all, she was only thinking of them. It was perfectly natural in a parent. Who wouldn't, offered half a chance? She was sure she'd be able to work a spell as simple as that. She'd seen Varius do it and it all looked perfectly simple to her. So she crept upstairs to his study

— she knew where he hid the key, she'd already spied on him — and she very cautiously opened the door and entered the forbidden room. It was like a treasure trove — books piled high against the walls. Vats of strange coloured liquid, glass jars with things in — she couldn't begin to guess what they were. Ugggh! Dusty bottles. Dusty dishes. An awful lot of dust.

Alicia Uggh!

Paul Finally, Alicia found what she was looking for. The spell book ...

Alicia (*thumbing the pages, muttering*) B for Beautiful ... Banshees ... Bats ... Beetle Juice ... Ah ... Beautiful ... Brackets see also Irresistible. Irresistible. Even better (*She turns more pages*) Incubi ... Invisibility ... Irresistible. To become Irresistible, prepare the following in a large jar ——

As Paul narrates Alicia assembles the ingredients, muttering to herself

Paul The mother worked feverishly for although she knew full well that her husband was away, she had the uneasy feeling that nonetheless someone, somewhere was watching her.

A cat meows. Alicia jumps

Alicia Out of the way, damn cat! Right. Stir the ingredients well. (*She does so*) Good. Now, pour the mixture over the pillow and inhale overnight. That's it then. That's it. Simple. Nothing to it.

Paul And the mother crept out of the study, being careful to re-lock the door and tiptoed along to her daughters' rooms, where she ever so gently, being careful not to wake them, poured the magic mixture on to each of their pillows.

Alicia (*softly*) There! Sleep well, my little beauties.

Paul In the morning, when the girls awoke and came down for breakfast, they seemed to Alicia no different than before.

Alicia (*muttering*) I must have got it wrong.

Paul But later on, when they both went for their stroll in the garden, she witnessed the results for herself.

The village boy comes on, catches sight of Cecilia and Emilia, grasps his throat and drops dead

Cecilia and Emilia walk on oblivious

The potion worked better than she'd dared hope.

The village boy exits

Alicia I must have made it a bit strong. Never mind.

Paul Over the next few days, Alicia decided to introduce her new irresistible daughters to a few possible suitors. It would be up to the girls themselves to choose the one they wanted to marry. After all, who could refuse them now? They were irresistible. So Alicia invited the kingdom's most eligible princes, all fabulously rich, good-looking young men from every corner of the realm.

Denzil comes strutting on, dressed up to the nines. He stands arrogantly. He catches sight of Emilia and his mouth drops open

Emilia (*smiling*) Hallo.

Denzil Arrgghhh!

Paul The potion really was most effective.

Cecilia (*smiling*) Hallo.

Denzil (*spinning round*) Arrrggg! Arrrgghh!

Paul In fact rather too effective ...

Emilia Here!

Cecilia No, here!

Emilia No, over here!

Cecilia Come on!

Emilia Come on!

Denzil spins this way and that, unable to choose between them. The girls continue to tease him

Paul The problem was, as Alicia soon discovered, that although the daughters were irresistible, gradually, they lost their hearts. And to each of their suitors they became as cold and uncharitable as the North Wind itself.

Cecilia and Emilia lead Denzil a dance

Alicia (*uneasily*) Now, girls, that's enough ...

Denzil Yes, please. Mercy ... I give in ...

Alicia You must let Prince Denzil sit down.

Cecilia We don't want him to sit down.

Alicia Why ever not?

Emilia Because he doesn't please us.

Cecilia He revolts us.

Emilia He disgusts us.

Cecilia He repels us.

Emilia He appals us.
Cecilia Go away.
Emilia Go away.
Denzil But, ladies, I beg you ...
Emilia ⎱ (*together*) GO AWAY!
Cecilia ⎰

Denzil rushes off, startled

The girls laugh

Alicia (*reproving*) Now that was no way to treat a crown prince was it, you
   naughty girls?
Paul But every prince was treated just the same — in fact, worse and worse ...
Alicia (*announcing*) Girls, look. Prince Basil is here.

Basil enters. He is as arrogant as the other one

Basil Good-afternoon, ladies, I — (*seeing the girls*) Aaarrgghhh!
Alicia These are my daughters.
Cecilia (*smiling*) Hallo, fatty.
Emilia (*smiling*) Hallo, ugly.
Basil (*spellbound*) Arrgghhh!
Alicia Now, now, girls. (*Whispering*) He's incredibly rich. Be nice to him.
Cecilia All right.
Emilia If you say so.
Cecilia Come here, spotty. Do you want to play a game, then?
Emilia Going to play a game, wart face?
Basil Anything, anything to please you, ladies.
Cecilia Blind man's buff.
Emilia Super.

Basil is blindfolded

Cecilia Don't wriggle.
Emilia Hold still, silly little man.
Basil You're both so beautiful.
Cecilia Of course we are. (*Sharply*) Don't touch me!
Emilia We know we are. (*Sharply*) Don't touch!
Cecilia (*spinning him around*) All right. Whichever one of us you can catch
   you can kiss.
Basil (*ecstatically*) Ah!

Emilia (*softly*) Maybe. (*Loudly*) Off you go, then.
Alicia Now, girls, you must let Basil catch one of you.
Cecilia Possibly.
Emilia Perhaps.
Cecilia Who knows? (*Calling*) Basil!
Emilia Who can tell? (*Calling*) Basil!

Basil reacts to their voices but they dodge him with ease. The girls exchange glances

Cecilia Hey! This way, podgy.
Emilia This way, lumpy.

They lure him towards an exit

Cecilia That's it.
Emilia That's the way.
Alicia Carefully, now, carefully.
Cecilia Come on, then. Run to me now, Basil.
Emilia Run to me, Basil.
Cecilia }
Emilia } (*together*) Now, Basil!

Basil rushes at them. They step aside at the last minute

Basil disappears

Alicia (*alarmed*) Oh, no!

A great cry off, as Basil falls. A splash

Cecilia Oh, dear!
Emilia He's fallen off the battlements.
Cecilia Into the moat.
Emilia Poor old Basil.
Cecilia (*calling*) Bad luck, Basil!
Alicia You naughty, naughty girls. You wicked girls, you did that deliberately. You're both of you heartless children. I've a good mind to give you no supper. You wait till your father gets back. He'll hear about this.
Cecilia We don't care.
Emilia We'll push him in the moat as well.
Cecilia See if we don't.

Alicia (*to herself*) Oh dear.

Paul But before their mother could say another word they had flounced away to torment more village boys. Alicia was horrified. For she realized that this was all her fault. And although she had threatened it, she was secretly quite frightened to think what Varius would say when he returned. He did, as I say, have a terrible temper when roused. So that night the mother once again crept into her husband's study and searched frantically for some antidote to the Irresistible spell. But she could find none.

Alicia (*desperately thumbing through the book*) Repellent ... Repulsive ... No, I can't use those. What if I got the strength wrong again? No-one would ever want to look at my lovely children then. Oh, what am I going to do? What shall I do?

Paul She could do nothing. And so the daughters, day by day, grew steadily more cruel and heartless without a single thought for anyone, man or woman. They destroyed marriages, they wrecked young love wherever they could; they stole grooms from brides, husbands from wives, only to discard them again instantly with never a second thought for the unhappiness they had caused. Far and wide hearts were broken. People lived in fear of them now. For not a single soul who loved or was in turn loved was any longer safe from this wicked pair. Then one day, word reached the family that a stranger had arrived in the kingdom. A prince, richer and more handsome than all other princes. What is more, he had asked to meet the irresistible daughters, for their fame by now had spread beyond the kingdom. Their mother was very excited.

Alicia Now, girls, this time, please ...

Cecilia (*casually*) All right. We'll see him ...

Emilia (*casually*) For a second ...

Cecilia Show him in then, Mother.

Alicia Oh dear. Don't do anything dreadful to him, will you? Do try. For me.

Alicia exits

Emilia What shall we do with this one then?

Cecilia Drown him?

Emilia Done that.

Cecilia Drive him mad with desire and make him jump into the fire.

Emilia Done that as well. Twice.

Cecilia Oh yes, so we have.

Emilia I know. We'll make him give us all his money ——

Cecilia By asking him trick questions ——

Emilia Which he could never answer ——

Cecilia Yes.

Emilia And then make him pay a forfeit ——
Cecilia Yes!
Emilia To — drink the moat.
Cecilia Through a straw.
Emilia Until he explodes.
Cecilia Yes. Shhh! He's coming.

Peter enters. He is still Varius but is masked and disguised. Alicia ushers him in

Alicia Girls, this is Prince Nemo.
Cecilia (*smiling*) Hallo.
Emilia (*smiling*) Hallo.
Peter (*as Varius, bowing*) Your servant, young ladies.
Cecilia (*puzzled, to Emilia*) Why didn't he go aaarrrggh?
Emilia (*puzzled, to Cecilia*) I don't know.
Cecilia What is it you want?
Emilia And why are you wearing a mask?
Peter I have come to pay court to you. The mask is so that you will not be influenced by my devastating good looks but only by the sincerity of my nature.
Cecilia (*to Emilia*) He thinks a lot of himself, doesn't he?
Emilia (*to Cecilia*) He certainly does. We'd better pull him down a peg or two, hadn't we? (*Loudly*) If you have come to pay court to us you must first prove your intelligence by answering two questions, one from each of us. Do you agree to that?
Peter I agree.
Alicia Simple questions now, girls.
Cecilia We have decided to be generous so you may have as many guesses as you like. But for every guess you make you must give us money. Do you agree?
Peter I agree.
Cecilia Very well. The first question shall be mine. It's very simple. You have merely to guess the date of my birth. But wait! The date and time to the exact second. For every second you are wrong you will pay me one piece of gold. For every minute, ten pieces of gold. For every hour a hundred. For every day a thousand. And for every year you are wrong a million pieces of gold. Do you agree?
Peter I agree.
Cecilia Proceed then. You have plenty of time.
Emilia Plenty of time.
Alicia Really, girls, that's quite impossible. Even I don't know ——

Cecilia Shhh, Mother!
Emilia Shhh!
Paul The strange prince appeared to think deeply for a moment.
Cecilia (*impatiently*) Come on!
Emilia (*impatiently*) Come on!
Peter Cecilia you were born eighteen years ago. On the thirty-ninth second of the fifty-first minute of the eighth hour of the fifteenth day of the seventh month.

A silence

Am I correct?
Cecilia (*shaken*) You might be.
Emilia (*softly*) He is, you know.
Alicia (*loudly*) He is. He's right. I remember now.
Paul There was no denying it, the unknown prince was absolutely correct.
Cecilia That was a very, very lucky guess indeed. You must now answer my sister's question.
Peter I will try.
Alicia Oh, girls, surely the prince has done enough —— ?
Emilia (*firmly*) Next question. Are you ready?
Peter I am ready.
Emilia Very well. Mine is also a simple problem. You have merely to guess my middle name. You may have as many guesses as you wish. For the first guess you pay me one piece of gold. For the second two pieces of gold. For the third, four. For the fourth, eight. For the fifth guess, sixteen. And so on. If you continue to guess wrongly or when you finally give up, then you pay the forfeit. Which I warn you will probably be your life. Now go ahead.

Silence

Aren't you going to have a guess?
Cecilia (*smirking*) Perhaps he can't think of any names.
Peter I was simply wondering.
Emilia Wonder away.
Peter I was wondering what could possibly be the middle name of a young woman so empty, so cold, so unfeeling, so heartless. Surely the answer is that, like her very self, there is nothing at the centre at all. Thus my answer to your question is equally simple. I look where your heart should be and find nothing there but emptiness. Likewise with your names. You have no middle name, Emilia.
Alicia He's right!

Emilia (*in fury*) How did you know that? Somebody told you. (*To Alicia*) You told him, didn't you? I'll get you for this.

Cecilia We'll get you for this.

Alicia No, no, girls. It wasn't me. I promise it wasn't me who told him.

Emilia Get her!

Cecilia Get her!

Alicia No!

The girls advance on their mother

Peter (*with a roar*) STOP!!!

A vast clap of thunder. The women freeze in their tracks. Peter removes his mask with a flourish

Alicia (*in a whisper*) Varius ...

Cecilia (*likewise*) Father ...

Emilia (*likewise*) Father ...

Peter stares at them. Another rumble of thunder

Alicia (*softly*) Your father is angry.

Peter I am. Very angry. And very sad. Sad that I am unable to trust my own family, my own wife. Unable to trust her not to meddle in things that do not concern her.

Alicia You know ... ?

Peter Of course I know, woman. Even though I was a thousand leagues away, I knew the very second you unlocked the door and stole into my study. Oh, Alicia ...

Alicia I'm sorry. It's all my fault. Don't blame the girls.

Peter I blame only myself. For allowing such greed, such vanity, to destroy my own family. The people I cared for most in the world ...

Cecilia What will happen to us?

Emilia What are you going to do to us, Father?

Cecilia Please don't punish us, we didn't mean ——

Peter Cecilia, you have created your own punishment, long ago. You have worshipped your looks and neglected your nature, child. Well, keep your looks for as long as they last. Indeed, you will need to fight to keep them. For I will tell you this. Anyone who loves you, will love only those looks. Once they tire of that beauty or it begins to fade, they will discover nothing beneath it but emptiness. And then and only then will they perceive the true beauty in your sister here. But too late. They will have already chosen.

Cecilia Oh.

Emilia And me? What about me?

Peter Emilia, you are condemned to live eternally in your sister's shadow. You have chosen to put aside your true beauty — in that case, let it remain for ever hidden where most men, being as they are, will never think to look for it. Instead, they will choose your worthless sister.

Emilia Oh.

Peter And for those foolish men themselves who cannot perceive beauty that is more than skin-deep: such asses by night deserve to be no more than donkeys by day. Let them bray away in a field until they finally come to their senses.

Alicia How long must this last?

Peter Until at least one of you loves selflessly and is herself selflessly loved.

More thunder

Alicia What about me? I'm your wife.

Peter Take your children and go, woman. I've finished with you.

Alicia Finished with me? What do you mean?

Peter Go!

Alicia It's pouring with rain ...

Cecilia Mother, come on ...

Emilia Mother ...

Alicia Don't I get any settlement? Any alimony? How do we live?

Peter Try working.

Alicia Work!

Cecilia Mother ...

Emilia Mother ...

Peter You'll be provided for, don't worry. Go on, leave me. Before I grow really angry.

A big clap of thunder

The women hurry out

Peter glares at the sky

Paul The sorcerer was as good as his word. He rehoused his family in number forty-nine Hollyhock Street. A pleasant little property but a bit of a come-down from a fifty bedroomed castle, I must admit. I suppose as sorcerers go he was fairly pleasant about it, but it has to be said that at the end of the day, they're not the easiest of people to live with. So — unforgiving, really.

Percy and Alicia enter

And with a long bitter sigh, Alicia finished her story. The end.

Peter (*taking over the narrative*) And Frederick, who had listened intently to all this, now fully understood the curse that had fallen on him when he had betrayed his wife.

Alicia Do you understand now, Frederick?

Percy Yes, I do.

Cecilia and Emilia enter. Emilia is consoling Cecilia

Peter ... he said, a trifle uneasily. For Frederick felt a deep sense of shame, not least because he had behaved so boringly and predictably just as the magician had prophesied he would.

Percy Oh fool, fool. (*He brays*)

Peter And he ran from the room past his wife and her sister. For he could no longer bear to look at either of them.

Percy gives a final bray as he exits. In a second the women also exit

And he sold the house and contents in Hollyhock Street, divided the cash, gave his wife custody of the water-colours and moved away to a dark, distant forest where he pooled resources with his sister and bought a large deserted mansion. And there he lived for the rest of his life, by day a donkey, by night a lonely bitter man with only Leonora for company. The end.

Paul, Frederick, Leonora, Yerp and Mrs Yerp enter

Percy (*taking up the narrative again*) And as Frederick finished his tale, the lights of the house came into view.

Paul What a remarkable story.

Leonora Every word of it is true, Rupert.

Paul I do not doubt it, Leonora. What is to be done, then?

Frederick There is nothing to be done. Nothing. Come, there are the lights of the house. Let us get out of this bitter cold.

Frederick, Leonora, Yerp and Mrs Yerp exit

Percy I could see that the brother had lapsed into his former gloom once again. Probably as a result of re-telling his tragic story. I was destined, anyway, to spend another night in that doom-laden house for it was now far too late to think of travelling. My poor brother and sister-in-law and my angelic little nieces and nephews would have to be disappointed; but with luck I would join them on Boxing Day although without, I fear, the presents I had intended for them, poor mites. It was my fervent hope that the villainous coachman, Gorff, was even now choking to death on my stolen sweetmeats and rich plum pudding. I slept fitfully that night, my dreams filled with warlocks and witches and donkeys and — yes, I have to confess — with Leonora whose divine countenance dominated everything. My bedroom overlooked the driveway and finally I was awoken by a heavy knocking on the front door.

Heavy knocking

And a few seconds later by excited, raised voices.

Mrs Yerp and Alicia, now playing an older Cecilia, enter

Mrs Yerp ... and I say you can't just barge your way in here, madam ...

Alicia Great heavens, woman, I've driven all night through the most appalling conditions. You have to let me in.

Percy I dressed quickly ...

Mrs Yerp The mistress is still abed and the master's — elsewhere. They can't be disturbed. You'll have to wait ...

Alicia Oh, this is impossible. You don't seem to realize how urgent this is.

Mrs Yerp Nothing to do with me ...

Paul May I be of assistance, Mrs Yerp?

Mrs Yerp It's all right, sir. It's not a problem. This here lady's just come visiting, that's all.

Alicia Ah, sir, I fear I do not know your name but please tell this — woman to let me in. I assure you my business is of a most urgent nature.

Paul I am Rupert Fellowes, at your service. May I enquire your name, madam?

Alicia My name, sir, is Mrs Cecilia Stringer if that means anything to you at all.

Percy I caught my breath.

Paul It certainly does, madam. Kindly let the lady pass, Mrs Yerp, I can vouch for her. Madam. I am but a guest here, yet I will see to it that Miss Stringer or her brother is awoken at once.

Alicia Sir, I thank you ...

Mrs Yerp They wouldn't want that, sir, I assure you ...

Leonora appears and soon, from another direction, Yerp

Percy But before I could argue further with the woman, Leonora appeared at the top of the stairs. I fear we had disturbed her.

Leonora What is the matter? Oh ——

Mrs Yerp Madam, this woman's been trying to ——

Paul This *lady*, Leonora, is none other than ——

Alicia I am Cecilia Stringer. You are Miss Leonora Stringer, are you not? I am your sister-in-law, Miss Stringer.

Leonora So it would appear. What do you want here?

Alicia To see Frederick. To see my husband.

Leonora He is no longer your husband.

Alicia Indeed ——

Leonora You have no relationship to this family any longer. I must ask you to leave.

Alicia But surely, you could not ——

Leonora Please leave, Miss Butterworth.

Alicia I am Mrs Stringer and I am staying until I have spoken to my husband.

Leonora He would not wish to see you, I assure you. Good-day. Mrs Yerp, please show this lady out.

Mrs Yerp Yes, madam.

Alicia Miss Stringer, I beg you. Please. Let me see him. Sir, if you have influence at all, intercede for me, I beg you.

Paul Leonora, I must plead on the lady's behalf. Her distress is pitiful to behold. I apologize if I seem to you ——

Leonora What would be the point, Rupert?

Paul There can be no harm in seeing him, surely. After all, it is past dawn and he is presumably ... What could be the harm? She has travelled a long way. Please. For my sake.

Leonora Very well, Rupert. For you, I will reluctantly grant her request.

Alicia Thank you, thank you.

Leonora It is against my better judgement, it must be said. Yerp, is the master ... ?

Yerp He's already out in the paddock, ma'am. He's had his hay.

Leonora Thank you. You will be able to see for yourself, Mrs Stringer, the depths of shame and indignity which your marriage has heaped upon my brother.

Alicia I realize. I already realize, believe me.

They all move out into the grounds

Percy We walked together to the paddock. I attempted to lift the mood of the party with some light conversation.

Paul You travelled alone, Mrs Stringer?

Alicia Yes, indeed. My sister Emilia would have accompanied me but my mother these days suffers from ill health and we could not leave her entirely alone.

Paul Nothing too serious I hope?

Alicia No, but she is of an age now, of course, when such things occur. But she still looks well and most days she is bright and cheerful. She has a naturally strong constitution which fortunately I have inherited. In fact, many observe that now I am older we are not dissimilar in looks.

Paul Then your mother must indeed be an attractive woman, Mrs Stringer.

Percy We reached the hidden door to the paddock.

Leonora I do not know what you intend to do now you are here, Mrs Stringer, but please be quick.

Alicia I will, Miss Stringer.

Percy Although I pride myself on being a normal, strong, masculine, unromantic man, the scene I was about to behold all but brought tears to my eyes.

They enter the paddock

Frederick enters as the donkey and stands, watching them

Alicia steps forward

Mrs Stringer and the donkey stood staring at each other. The woman wore an expression of such tender and touching sadness, it was almost unbearable to behold. As for the donkey, at first it seemed that he failed to recognize her. Until ——

Frederick brays loudly

The creature let out such a bellow that could only be interpreted as one great joyous cry of greeting.

Alicia Frederick!

Alicia runs forward and embraces Frederick

Percy Without another word, the woman rushed forward to embrace the creature, wrapping her arms around its neck and kissing it passionately on the muzzle. In an instant a remarkable and miraculous transformation took place. Where once the dumb creature had been, restored to his natural

shape and size now stood the joyful figure of Frederick.
Frederick Cecilia!
Alicia Frederick, oh, Frederick.

They embrace. The whole group are now somewhat overwhelmed

Percy I have to report that I was not the only one to be moved by these events.
Alicia Oh, Frederick. You didn't forget me?
Frederick How could I forget, Cecilia? Forgive me.
Alicia With all my heart.

They embrace again

Percy Indeed, so moved was I by this sight and also anxious not to embarrass the reunited couple, that I turned to make some light conversation with Leonora.
Paul Miss Stringer, may I ask you ——
Leonora Oh, yes, yes, yes, Rupert. My answer can be none other than yes!

She throws herself into Paul's arms. After a second he responds

Percy There had been, it seemed, a small social misunderstanding between us, but one that I was more than happy to overlook. The habit, moreover, appeared to be catching.
Yerp Oh, Mrs Yerp!
Mrs Yerp Mr Yerp.

They too embrace

Peter enters as Varius

Paul At that moment, hovering in the sky, the spirit of Varius, the sorcerer appeared.
Peter Cecilia, you have at last found unselfish love. The spell is now broken.

Thunder

Percy Just a minute, who's telling this story ... ?
Peter And as for Emilia, she too was finally free to find true love ...

Emilia enters

And she did so almost immediately with a certain Albert Haskins a few doors down at number twenty-five Hollyhock Street. A very eligible bachelor who not only worked for the gas board but was an extremely accomplished ballroom dancer ...

Percy (*indignantly*) Look, what is going on here?

Peter But the main reason Emilia loved Albert Haskins was that he looked exactly like the younger version of her sister Cecilia's husband, Frederick.

Emilia (*looking at Percy and holding out her arms*) Darling!

Percy (*not prepared to argue*) Oh, all right then, what the hell ... (*He runs down to join her*) Darling!

They embrace

Cecilia enters

Paul And as for Varius himself, well, wouldn't you know it, he ran off with a girl who was young enough to be his daughter ——

Cecilia (*running to Peter*) Darling!

Peter Darling!

They embrace

Paul But then sorcerers have all the luck.

Percy So finally, remember this, ladies and gentlemen, if you will ...

Peter Whichever way you look at it ...

Paul Whichever story you choose to believe ...

Percy (*indicating Peter*) His ...

Peter (*indicating Paul*) Or his ...

Paul (*indicating Percy*) Or his ...

Percy However they may start ...

Peter However they might continue ...

Paul You'll find they all tend to finish up much the same in the end ——

Percy — the end ——

Peter — the end ——

Paul — the end ——

All — THE END!

The keyboard player strikes up some music. The company dance and bow

CURTAIN

FURNITURE AND PROPERTY LIST

Further dressing may be added at the director's discretion. Extra properties are contained in the prop bags. It is possible, indeed preferable, that many of the furniture and property effects are mimed or suggested with lighting.

ACT I

On stage: Piano (at the side or in the orchestra pit)

Off stage: Suitcase of props (**Percy**)
Box of props (**Peter**)
Second suitcase of props (**Percy**)
Bag of props. *In it:* two baby-like bundles (for **Cecilia** in Act II) (**Paul**)
Second box of props (**Peter**)
Second bag of props. *In it:* dusty bottles and dishes, etc., spell book, ingredients for spell (for **Alicia** in Act II), blindfold (for **Cecilia** and **Emilia** in Act II) (**Paul**)
Chaise-longue (**Leonora**)
Cards, etc. (**Actors**)
Blanket (**Mrs Yerp**)
Dining-table (**Yerp**)
Three chairs (**Mrs Yerp**)
Food, serving dishes, etc. for dinner (**Yerp** and **Mrs Yerp**)
Frederick's dinner — grass and thistles in a silver salver (**Mrs Yerp**)
Food, serving dishes, etc. for breakfast (**Yerp** and **Mrs Yerp**)
Lanterns (**Leonora, Yerp** and **Mrs Yerp**)

Personal: **Percy**: contract
Peter: contract
Paul: contract

ACT II

Strike:	Deepwood House furniture (NB: **Percy**, **Peter** and **Paul**'s prop bags must remain on stage)
Set:	Various chairs to be used throughout Act II
Off stage:	Tiny parcels (**Cecilia**) Small tea table. *On it:* tea things (**Alicia**) Portfolio of bad water-colours (**Cecilia**) Wedding fabrics and parcels (**Alicia** and **Emilia**) Book and sewing kit (**Cecilia**) Small suitcase (**Cecilia**) Ball (**Cecilia** and **Emilia**)

LIGHTING PLOT

A space representing interior and exterior settings.

Practical fittings required: lanterns

ACT I

To open:	Full stage lighting	
Cue 1	**Percy**: " ... tragic Victorian tale entitled, *The Donkey.*" *Change to wood/Deepwood House effect*	(Page 12)
Cue 2	**Percy**: " — I caught sight of something." *Distant glimmer of lamplight; gradually change lights to reveal doorway of Deepwood House*	(Page 15)
Cue 3	**Percy**: "When I awoke it was dark ..." *Darkness effect*	(Page 27)
Cue 4	**Leonora, Yerp** and **Mrs Yerp** enter with lanterns *Lantern effect*	(Page 27)
Cue 5	**Percy** finishes his story *Revert to original state*	(Page 28)

ACT II

To open: Full stage lighting

No cues

Note: Other lighting changes — to suggest changes in locale — are made at the discretion of the director.

EFFECTS PLOT

All the music cues in the text refer to live music provided by the keyboard player

ACT I

Cue 1   **Percy:** " ... knocked upon the door."   (Page 15)
          Hollow knocking effect

Cue 2   **Percy:** " ... before anyone answered."   (Page 15)
          Rattling of chains and bolts

Cue 3   **Percy:** " ... that awoke me just before dawn."   (Page 22)
          Distant braying of a donkey
            (Note: this cue may be performed live by **Frederick**)

Cue 4   **Paul** lies back in bed   (Page 22)
          Cock crow

ACT II

Cue 5   **Percy** and **Cecilia** sit, reading and sewing   (Page 43)
          Clock striking effect

Cue 6   **Paul:** " ... somewhere was watching her."   (Page 52)
          Cat meow effect

Cue 7   Great cry from **Basil**, off   (Page 55)
          Splash

Cue 8   **Peter:** "STOP!!!"   (Page 59)
          Thunder clap

Cue 9   **Emilia:** "Father ..."   (Page 59)
          Another rumble of thunder

Cue 10   **Peter:** " ... and is herself selflessly loved."   (Page 60)
          More thunder

Cue 11   **Peter:** "Before I grow really angry."   (Page 60)
          A big clap of thund

Cue 12	**Percy**: " ... a heavy knocking on the front door." *Heavy knocking effect*	(Page 61)
Cue 13	**Peter**: "The spell is now broken." *Thunder*	(Page 65)